big NATE

big NATE
FROM THE TOP

by LINCOLN PEIRCE

SCHOLASTIC INC.
New York Toronto London Auckland
Sydney Mexico City New Delhi Hong Kong

ISBN 978-0-545-34500-2

12 11 10 9 8 7 11 12 13 14 15 16/0

Printed in the U.S.A. 23

First Scholastic printing, January 2011

These strips appeared in newspapers from August 28, 2006, through April 1, 2007.

**To JDP,
the original Big Nate**

DAD, DO YOU HAVE TO TAG ALONG? CAN'T I SHOP FOR BACK-TO-SCHOOL CLOTHES MYSELF?
SORRY, NATE...
I'M JUST NOT SURE I CAN TRUST YOU TO BUY YOUR OWN SLACKS.
WELL, WHY SHOULD WE TRUST YOU? YOU'LL MAKE ME BUY SOMETHING DORKY!
ME? NO, I WON'T! WHAT MAKES YOU SAY THAT?
LET'S START WITH THE FACT THAT YOU CALL THEM "SLACKS".
OKAY, WHATEVER! TROUSERS!
8
28
Peirce

THESE LOOK GOOD!
ARE YOU KIDDING ME? THEY'RE BROWN!
BUT THEY'RE JEANS! YOU LIKE JEANS, DON'T YOU?
YEAH, WHEN THEY'RE BLUE! HENCE THE NAME: BLUE JEANS!
PUT 'EM BACK, DAD! THOSE ARE THE UGLIEST PANTS I'VE EVER SEEN!
OKAY, OKAY. PLAIN BROWN IS PRETTY DRAB.
8/29
© 2006 by NEA, Inc.
NOW WE'RE TALKIN'! BROWN PLAID!
DAD, HAS IT OCCURRED TO YOU THAT THERE'S A REASON THESE ITEMS ARE IN THE BARGAIN BIN?
Peirce

HOLD IT, HOLD IT. WHERE ARE YOU GOING?
TO TRY THESE PANTS ON.
I DON'T THINK SO, NATE! THEY'VE GOT HOLES IN THEM!
THAT'S THE STYLE, DAD! LET GO!
I WON'T PAY FOR A PAIR OF PANTS THAT ARE RIPPED ALREADY!
8/30
YES YOU WILL.
YES I WILL.
NICE MOVE, DAD.
Peirce

I'M STARTING TO HAVE THOSE NIGHTMARES AGAIN.
WHAT NIGHT-MARES?
ABOUT GOING BACK TO SCHOOL! WHEN-EVER I CLOSE MY EYES, I SEE MRS. GODFREY'S UGLY FACE!
8/31
!
DON'T WORRY ABOUT IT.
GAH!
NOW, IF YOU START SEEING HER FACE WHILE YOU'RE **AWAKE**, THEN YOU'VE GOT PROB-LEMS.
Peirce

WHAT'S WITH NATE?
HE'S HALLUCINATING. HE KEEPS SEEING MRS. GODFREY'S FACE EVERYWHERE.
9/1
HEH HEH.
THAT'S PRETTY FUNNY.
HEH HEH HA HA HA HA HO HA
HAH HA HEH HA
WA HA HA HA HA HA OH HO HO HA HA WA HA HA HO HA HA HA HA HA HA
I'M A SICK, SICK BOY.
Peirce

DAD, WHERE'S THE THERMOMETER?
I'M NOT SURE.
9/2
I DON'T FEEL VERY WELL.
REALLY?
LET ME FEEL YOUR FOREHEAD.
© 2006 by NEA, Inc.
NO!
?
peirce

AHHH! THE ANNUAL RITUAL! BUYING A NEW SCHOOL BINDER!
... BUT IT CAN'T BE JUST **ANY** BINDER! IT'S GOT TO HAVE ALL THE LATEST FEATURES!
A REINFORCED SPINE WITH QUICK-LOCK RINGS!
EXPANDABLE POCKETS WITH VELCRO FASTENERS!
YAWN
A REMOVABLE MESH PENCIL CASE WITH A BONUS CELL PHONE COMPARTMENT!
WHAT ABOUT **YOU**, NATE? DON'T **YOU** NEED A NEW BINDER?
YEAH, I GUESS I DO.
WHAK!
I'LL TAKE IT.
Peirce

LAST DAY OF SUMMER VACATION! WHAT SHOULD WE DO?
9/4
© 2006 by NEA, Inc.
I DON'T KNOW, BUT DOWN THE ROAD THE WEATHER GODS OWE US BIG TIME.

A PRINCIPAL IS NEVER QUITE SO EXCITED AS ON THE FIRST DAY OF SCHOOL!
THERE'S A FEELING OF RENEWAL, A SENSE OF...
IS IT TRUE? IS IT TRUE?
OOP. GUESS NOT.
GUYS, HE'S STILL HERE.
SIGH...
9/5
© 2006 by NEA, Inc.
Peirce

Do you recall that night in June
You watched the comet fly?
And can you picture,
In your mind,
That ballgame in July?
Do you remember mini-golf,
And all those putts you missed?
! !
Then how could you forget about
Your summer reading list?
MRS. GODFREY
© 2006 by NEA, Inc.
9/6
Peirce

MRS. GODFREY, GIVING ME DETENTION FOR NOT COMPLETING THE SUMMER READING LIST ISN'T FAIR! WHY SINGLE ME OUT?
I MEAN... CHUCKLE! SURELY I'M NOT THE ONLY ONE WHO DIDN'T FINISH! RIGHT, GANG?
GANG?
WHAT EVER HAPPENED TO SOLI-DARITY?
I FINISHED IT ON JUNE FIFTEENTH.
© 2006 by NEA, Inc.
Peirce

WHAT'S THE PROBLEM, NATE? WHY WON'T YOU SIT STILL?
I CAN'T HELP IT! I'M HOT!
FIDGET FIDGET FIDGET
I'VE BEEN WEARING SHORTS ALL SUMMER, AND NOW I'VE GOT TO WEAR LONG PANTS! I FEEL LIKE I'M IN A SAUNA!
9/8
I'VE GOT THE WORST CASE OF "ITCHY THIGHS" I'VE EVER HAD!
TOO MUCH INFORMATION, SON.
I MEAN, DOES ANYTHING CHAFE LIKE MOIST DENIM?
Peirce
© 2006 by NEA, Inc.

I CAN'T TAKE MUCH MORE OF THIS. I REALLY CAN'T.
I'M SO, SO SICK OF SCHOOL. I ABSOLUTELY HATE IT.
DUDE, ARE YOU SERIOUS?
9/9
IT'S OUR **FIRST DAY!** CAN'T YOU WAIT UNTIL LATER IN THE YEAR TO GET ALL BURNED OUT?
NO.
WHEN YOU GET HIT BY A TRAIN, IT'S NOT THE CABOOSE THAT KILLS YOU.
IBRARY
peirce

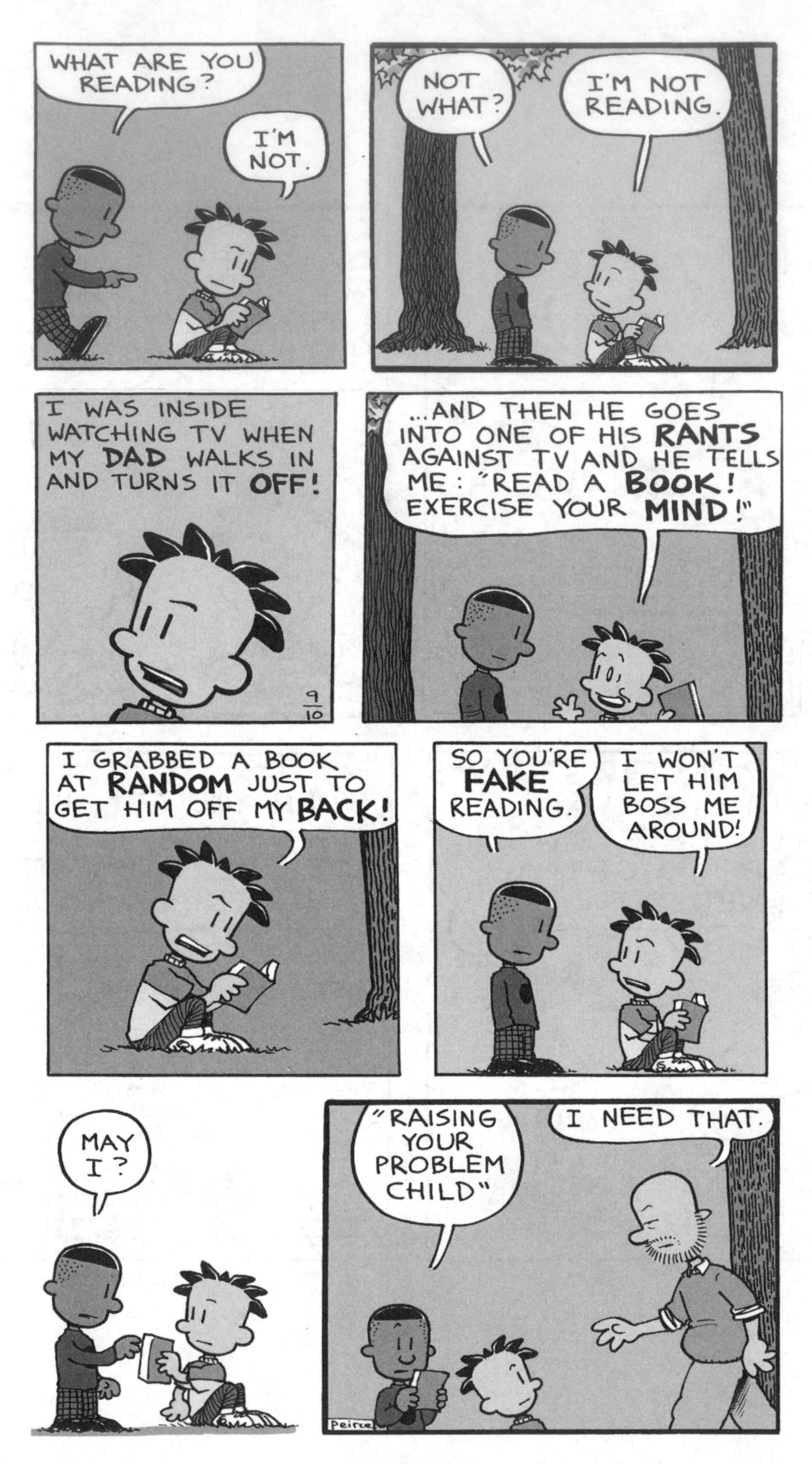
WHAT ARE YOU READING?
I'M NOT.
NOT WHAT?
I'M NOT READING.
I WAS INSIDE WATCHING TV WHEN MY DAD WALKS IN AND TURNS IT OFF!
9/10
...AND THEN HE GOES INTO ONE OF HIS RANTS AGAINST TV AND HE TELLS ME: "READ A BOOK! EXERCISE YOUR MIND!"
I GRABBED A BOOK AT RANDOM JUST TO GET HIM OFF MY BACK!
SO YOU'RE FAKE READING.
I WON'T LET HIM BOSS ME AROUND!
MAY I?
"RAISING YOUR PROBLEM CHILD"
I NEED THAT.
Peirce

AH! NATE! HALLO, MY FRIEND!
OH. HEY, ARTUR.
I DID NOT HEAR FROM YOU DURING SUMMER, NATE! YOU DID NOT WRITING TO ME AT MY GRAND-PARENTS' HOUSE!
UH... WELL, I DIDN'T HAVE YOUR ADDRESS THERE.
9/11
BUT YES! BECAUSE I GAVE TO YOU IN JUNE AT END OF SCHOOL!
UM... RIGHT, BUT I COULDN'T READ YOUR HAND-WRITING.
© 2006 by NEA, Inc.
BUT... TO PRINT ADDRESS, I TYPED USING COMPUTER!
I HATE THIS KID.
Peirce

NATE. HERE. I BROUGHT TO YOU SOUVENIR FROM MY TRIP TO BELARUS.
WOW, A SNOW GLOBE! I COL-LECT THESE!
9/12
YES. AND ON BOTTOM SAYS IT "BELARUS", SO YOU KNOW IS REALLY FROM THERE!
WOW... UH... HERE, I GOT A SOUVENIR FOR YOU TOO, ARTUR...
AH.
A PENCIL!
© 2006 by NEA, Inc.
Peirce
SO YOU WERE TO VISITING SOME-WHERE CALLED "TICON-DEROGA"?
RIGHT. NICE TOWN.

I DON'T GET IT. WHY IS ARTUR AL-WAYS SO NICE TO ME?
BECAUSE HE'S A NICE KID, THAT'S WHY!
BUT WHY WASTE YOUR TIME BEING NICE TO SOMEONE WHO CAN'T STAND YOU? WHAT'S UP WITH THAT?
WELL, SOME PEOPLE...
OOP! HOLD ON!
9/13
© 2006 by NEA, Inc.
JENNY, M'LADY!
SOME PEOPLE ARE JUST KIND OF CLUE-LESS.
Peirce

HOW DO YOU DO IT?
DO WHAT?
WE'VE BEEN BACK IN SCHOOL LESS THAN A WEEK, AND ALREADY YOUR LOCKER IS FILLED WITH JUNK!
JUNK? JUNK?
9/14
DOES THIS LOOK LIKE JUNK TO YOU?
A FABERGÉ EGG?
CAREFUL WITH THAT. IT'S BREAKABLE.
Peirce
© 2006 by NEA, Inc.

LET'S SAY YOU JUST FOUND OUT YOU HAVE ONLY 24 HOURS TO LIVE. WHAT WOULD YOU DO?
HOW WOULD YOU SPEND YOUR LAST DAY ON EARTH?
WELL, THAT WOULD DEPEND ON WHAT DAY IT WAS.
WHY WOULD IT MATTER?
IT WOULD MATTER IF IT WAS A SUNDAY. SUNDAY'S MY TV NIGHT.
OF COURSE, IF "FAMILY GUY" WAS A RERUN, THAT WOULD BE A DIFFERENT STORY.
9/15
© 2006 by NEA, Inc.
Peirce

DAD, HOW COME WE NEVER GO ANY-WHERE?
LIKE WHERE?
SOME-PLACE FUN! LIKE DISNEY WORLD!
BECAUSE IT'S WAY TOO EXPENSIVE!
JUST THE PLANE FARE FOR THREE PEOPLE WOULD BE...
WHOA, WHOA! WHY THREE PEOPLE?
CAN'T WE LEAVE SOMEONE AT HOME?
DON'T TEMPT ME.
WINKA WINKA BLINKA
Peirce

WHY WAS ABRAHAM LINCOLN KNOWN AS "HONEST ABE"? NATE?
HM?
UHHH...
IT WAS PART OF YOUR ASSIGNED READING.
9/17
RIGHT, RIGHT...
DID YOU EVEN DO THE READING?
YES, I DID THE READING!
WELL, THEN YOU SHOULD KNOW THE ANSWER.
BUT YOU DIDN'T TELL US YOU WERE GOING TO ASK US ABOUT IT!
SO YOU ONLY PAY ATTENTION TO THE READING IF YOU KNOW I'M GOING TO ASK YOU ABOUT IT?
OF COURSE!
UH... KOFF! ...NOT!! OF COURSE NOT IS WHAT I... UH... MEANT TO... SAY...
YOU KNOW, THERE'S SUCH A THING AS BEING TOO HONEST.
PRINCIPA
Peirce

OKAY, GANG, LET'S JUMP ON 'EM EARLY! GET OUT THERE!
COACH
UH... NATE, TIME TO TAKE THE FIELD.
JUST A SEC, COACH.
NARF NARF
9/18
I'LL NEED LOTS OF ENERGY FOR THE GAME, SO I'M EATING A TWELVE-PACK OF "POWER BARS"!
NARF NARF
CHOMP CHOMPF
THE WEIRD THING IS, NOW I'M ACTUALLY FEELING A LITTLE SLUGGISH.
CRIPES.
COACH
Peirce

GAME'S STARTING, 'KEEP! GET IN THE GOAL!
YEAH. OKAY.
HEY, YOU OKAY, SON? YOU LOOK A LITTLE GREEN!
I ATE TOO MANY POWER BARS.
7/19
AH! I HEAR YOU, CHAMP. I'VE BEEN THERE, BE-LIEVE ME.
I REMEMBER ONCE, I HAD THIS LIVER AND CHEESE GRINDER THAT WAS JUST **OOZING** GREASE...
HOOOLP!
Peirce

OKAY, SO YOUR STOMACH DOESN'T FEEL SO GOOD! SUCK IT UP! **DEAL** WITH IT!
ONCE YOU SEE A LITTLE ACTION, YOU'LL FORGET ALL ABOUT IT!
9/20
WHUMP!
...OR PERHAPS NOT.
WE'LL NEED THE BALL, SON.
Peirce

GAAH! EVERY TIME A CLOUD GOES BY, I'M **FREEZING**!
...AND WHEN THE SUN COMES OUT AGAIN, I'M **BOILING**!
9/21
DOOF!
© 2006 by NEA, Inc.
THEN THERE'S THE ISSUE OF THESE RECURRING HEADACHES...
Peirce

OH, NO!
9/22
GOTTA GET TO IT BEFORE ANYONE ELSE DOES!
YAAAAH!
© 2006 by NEA, Inc.
HA! DIBS ON THE LAST JUICE BOX!
WHATEVER.
Peirce

A goalie, or a "keeper",
(As we keepers like to say),
Is the most important person
On the soccer field of play.
9/23
He must make acrobatic saves,
The most athletic kind!
He must be fearless,
Quick, alert, and . . .
Okay, never mind.
© 2006 by NEA, Inc.
Peirce

THERE'S A COOL-LOOKING CLOUD...
A FLOCK OF GEESE...
AN AIRPLANE...
A HOT AIR BALLOON!...
A BUTTERFLY...
9
24
BOOF!
...AND LOTS AND LOTS OF TWINKLY LITTLE STARS!...
EASY, SON. HOW MANY FINGERS AM I HOLDING UP?
COACH
Peirce

AH! FOR ONCE, I'M READY FOR SCHOOL PICTURE DAY!
I'M NOT GOING TO LET THE SCHOOL PICTURE GUY CATCH ME WITH A STUPID EXPRESSION ON MY FACE! I'VE BEEN **PRACTICING!**
PRACTICING?
HOW DO YOU **PRACTICE** FOR A **PICTURE?**
YOU PRACTICE YOUR **LOOK!** I NOW HAVE MY OWN PERSONAL **LOOK!**
9/25
© 2006 by NEA, Inc.
...AND HERE IT IS.
VERY NATURAL.
I THOUGHT THE POINT WAS TO **NOT** LOOK STUPID.
Peirce

NATE, THIS EXPRESSION YOU'RE GOING TO USE FOR YOUR SCHOOL PIC-TURE IS RIDICULOUS.
TURES
OH YEAH?
YOU DON'T EVEN LOOK LIKE YOUR-SELF! THAT'S NOT YOUR REAL SMILE!
IT'S NOT EVEN A SMILE, REALLY.
6TH GRA LINE UP
9/26
YEAH, IT'S MORE LIKE A SMIRK.
A DORKY SMIRK.
6TH GRADE LINE UP HE
© 2006 by NEA, Inc.
IT'S A SMORK!
...WITH JUST A TOUCH OF CONSTIPATION!
6TH GRAD LINE UP
Peirce

HI, SCHOOL PICTURE GUY.
AH! WHAT'S UP, KID? WHAT'S THE GOOD WORD?
NOBODY LIKES MY "LOOK."
HMM... I SEE, I SEE.
WELL, THEY MAY HAVE A POINT, AMIGO. THE HAIR-STYLE **IS** A BIT EXTREME.
9/27
© 2006 by NEA, Inc.
I HAVEN'T EVEN SHOWN YOU THE "LOOK" YET!!
OOP. MY BAD, KID. CARRY ON.
Peirce

OKAY, KID, SHOW ME THIS "LOOK" YOU'RE ALL FIRED UP ABOUT.
OKAY. I THINK IT'S PRETTY GOOD.
I JUST TRY TO... YOU KNOW... ACT CASUAL.
9/28
KID, I HAVEN'T SEEN SUCH ACTING SINCE THE HEYDAY OF MR. KEVIN COSTNER.
WHO?
"WATERWORLD." GAD, WHAT A WASTE OF TWO HOURS OF MY LIFE!
Peirce

KID, YOU WANT A PICTURE THAT LOOKS GOOD IN THE YEARBOOK? LOSE THAT CHEESEBALL EXPRESSION ON YOUR MUG!
BUT...
JUST BE YOURSELF, CHUM! DON'T CHASE AFTER SOME BOGUS STANDARDS IMPOSED BY SOCIETY!
9/29
SOCIETY?
PERHAPS A TALE FROM MY OWN PAST WILL HELP ILLUMINATE MY POINT!
© 2006 by NEA, Inc.
WHATEVER HAPPENED TO "SAY CHEESE"?
IT WAS RAINING THE NIGHT OF THE "STAR TREK" CONVENTION...
Peirce

AHHH, THERE WE GO, KID! NOW THAT'S A NATURAL-LOOKING SMILE!
I SEE A BIT OF THE ROGUE IN YOU, LAD! A BIT OF THE YOUNG JAMES T. KIRK, AS PLAYED BY THE ONE AND ONLY BILL SHATNER!
OF COURSE, NOW HE'S GOT EMMYS OUT THE WAZOO FOR "BOSTON LEGAL", BUT BEFORE THAT, HIS WORK ON "T.J. HOOKER" WAS...
JUST TAKE THE PIC-TURE!!
KLICK!
9/30
© 2006 by NEA, Inc.
Peirce

HERE'S AN EXPRESSION THAT PROVES DOGS ARE BETTER THAN CATS!
"WORKING LIKE A DOG"!
WORKING LIKE A DOG.
IT MEANS DOGS ARE HARD-WORKING! UNLIKE CATS!
CATS JUST SIT AROUND LICKING THEMSELVES! BUT DOGS ARE OUT THERE DOING STUFF!
10/1
THEY'RE RUNNING AROUND! FETCHING STICKS! DIGGING HOLES! CATS JUST SLEEP ALL DAY!
YOU'LL NEVER HEAR ANYONE USE THE EXPRESSION "WORKING LIKE A CAT"!
TRIP!
THERE'S ANOTHER EXPRESSION: "DOGGING IT"!
Z
GET UP, SPITSY.
PEIRCE

I'D LIKE TO RUN FOR STUDENT GOVERNMENT, BUT I DON'T KNOW WHICH OFFICE TO TRY FOR.
GINA for PRESIDENT
VOTE
WELL, FORGET ABOUT PRESIDENT. GINA'S GOT THAT ONE SEWN UP.
OH, COME ON! I BET I COULD BEAT GINA!
YOU TRIED TO BEAT HER LAST YEAR, FOOL! YOU CAME IN THIRD!
HEY, THIRD'S NOT SO BAD!
THERE WERE ONLY TWO OF YOU RUNNING.
YOU WERE EDGED OUT BY A WRITE-IN CAMPAIGN FOR STEWIE FROM "FAMILY GUY."
10/2
Peirce

I DON'T WANT TO RUN FOR PRESIDENT, BECAUSE GINA'S GOING TO BE PRESIDENT.
...AND BEING VICE PRESIDENT WOULD MEAN GETTING BOSSED AROUND BY GINA... SO THAT'S OUT. ...AND RUNNING FOR SECRETARY SOUNDS TOO GIRLISH...
10/3
I GUESS I'LL JUST HAVE TO SETTLE FOR TREASURER.
PEIRCE
"I'LL JUST HAVE TO SETTLE FOR TREASURER." THERE'S AN INSPIRING CAMPAIGN SLOGAN!
EXCUSE ME WHILE I RUSH TO THE POLLS!

FASTEN YOUR SEAT BELT, SHEILA! I'M RUNNING AGAINST YOU FOR TREASURER!
YOU? REALLY?
YUP, AND I CAN'T WAIT TO GET ELECTED! MY ALLOWANCE JUST DOESN'T GO AS FAR AS IT USED TO!
WHAT? WHOA, **WHOA**!
10/4
NATE! YOU CAN'T RAID THE SIXTH GRADE TREASURY FOR YOUR **PERSONAL USE**!!
WELL, **DUH**! I **REALIZE** THAT, SHEILA!
© 2006 by NEA, Inc.
ALL I'M SAYING IS, THE SALARY WILL COME IN HANDY!
UH... MORE BAD NEWS, CHAMP...
Peirce

I'VE DECIDED NOT TO RUN FOR STUDENT GOVERNMENT.
WHAT CHANGED YOUR MIND?
WELL, YOU DON'T REALLY **DO** ANYTHING IN STUDENT GOVERNMENT! YOU DON'T HAVE ANY **POWER**!
WHAT'S THE POINT IN RUNNING FOR OFFICE IF IT DOESN'T GIVE ME **POWER**? ... OR MONEY?
10/5
...OR FAME. FAME IS GOOD.
THERE'S NOTHING LIKE PUBLIC SERVICE.
CERTAINLY NOT IN THIS CASE.
Peirce

HELLO, BOYS!
HI, MR. ROSA.
NATE, I UNDERSTAND YOU'RE RUNNING FOR STUDENT GOVERNMENT!
NO, I CHANGED MY MIND.
OH? WHY?
I JUST DECIDED NOT TO RUN, THAT'S ALL.
10/6
HE FOUND OUT MIDDLE SCHOOL TREASURERS CAN'T PRINT THEIR OWN MONEY.
NOT A LOT OF MONEY! JUST ENOUGH SO I WOULDN'T HAVE TO HOLD A BAKE SALE!
Peirce

WHAT A SHAME I WON'T BE RUNNING FOR STUDENT GOVERNMENT!
YOU SOUND BUMMED OUT.
OH, I'M NOT BUMMED OUT FOR **ME!** I'M BUMMED OUT FOR OUR **CLASSMATES!**
10/7
THEY'LL BE DEPRIVED OF MY LEADER-SHIP!
LEADER-SHIP?
© 2006 by NEA, Inc.
THE SAME LEADER-SHIP YOU DISPLAYED DURING OUR CAMP-ING TRIP LAST SUMMER?
DOYYYY! "FOLLOW **ME**, GUYS! THE TENT'S **THIS** WAY!"
Peirce

MRS. GODFREY, I'M LODGING A PROTEST!
ABOUT WHAT?
THIS "CURRENT EVENTS" TEST! THE WAY YOU GRADED IT IS TOTALLY UNFAIR!
I MEAN, I KNOW I DIDN'T ACE EVERY QUESTION, BUT DID I REALLY DE-SERVE A C?
LET ME SEE.
HMMM...
MM HMM...
HMM...
10/8
YOU'RE RIGHT, NATE. YOU DON'T DESERVE A C.
THIS IS A D-MINUS IF I'VE EVER SEEN ONE.
OH, HOW I HATE HER.
JUST AN F.Y.I: PRESIDENT BUSH'S BROTHER IS NAMED "JEB", NOT "REGGIE."
Peirce

MRS. CZERWICKI, WHY DOESN'T THE SCHOOL JAZZ UP THIS ROOM A LITTLE?
IT'S SO **DRAB** IN HERE, YOU KNOW? I MEAN, IT'S LIKE A **DEAD ZONE!**
10/9
PAINT THE WALLS! PUT UP SOME POSTERS! MAKE PEOPLE **WANT** TO BE HERE!
© 2006 by NEA, Inc.
NATE, MAKING PEOPLE WANT TO BE IN THE DETENTION ROOM ISN'T REALLY THE POINT.
WELL, PERSONALLY, I LIKE A PLACE TO FEEL HOMEY.
peirce

CHESTER, MY MAN! WHAT ARE YOU IN FOR?
NOTHING. IT'S NOT FAIR.
10/10
OH, COME ON, BIG FELLA! YOU CAN TELL ME!
I DIDN'T DO NOTHING.
BUT YOU MUST HAVE DONE SOMETHING, CHESTER! YOU DON'T GET DETENTION FOR NO REASON!
© 2006 by NEA, Inc.
I DIDN'T DO NOTHING.
...AND, ON YOUR BEHALF, I'M OUT-RAGED.
Peirce

HOW COME THEY KEEP GIVING ME DETENTION?
I'LL TELL YOU WHY, CHESTER!
IT'S BECAUSE YOU KEEP REPEATING THE SAME BEHAVIOR! OF **COURSE** THEY'RE GOING TO KEEP GIVING YOU DETENTION!
DOING THE SAME THINGS OVER AND OVER AGAIN AND EXPECTING DIFFERENT RESULTS IS THE DEFINITION OF...
10/11
OF WHAT?
...OF SOMEONE WHO IS COMPLETELY, TRAGICALLY MISUNDERSTOOD.
Peirce

MRS. CZERWICKI, I'D LIKE TO SPEAK UP ON BEHALF OF CHESTER OVER THERE.
HE SAYS HE'S BEEN GIVEN DETENTION FOR NO GOOD REASON, AND I BELIEVE HIM!
HE'S DONE NOTHING WRONG!
NOTHING WRONG?
THIS IS HIS DETENTION REPORT.
ULES
© 2006 by NEA, Inc.
10 12
YOUR REPORT CONSISTS OF THREE X-RAYS AND A RESTRAINING ORDER, SO I'M GUESSING YOU'LL BE HERE AWHILE.
Peirce

HEY. GO ASK MRS. CZERWICKI TO LET ME OUT OF HERE.
CHESTER, I ALREADY TRIED ONCE! IT WON'T DO ANY GOOD!
YOU SENT SOME KID TO THE EMERGENCY ROOM!
HE STARTED IT.
WHATEVER! BOTTOM LINE, YOU PUT A BEAT-DOWN ON HIM! YOU DON'T HAVE A LEG TO STAND ON!
10/13
© 2006 by NEA, Inc.
NEITHER DOES THE OTHER KID. HA HA.
YOU'RE A RIOT, CHESTER.
Peirce

WHO'S THIS IN THE PHOTO, MRS. CZERWICKI?
THAT'S MY DAUGHTER.
10/14
AND THAT GUY NEXT TO HER IS HER HUSBAND, I GUESS?
HUSBAND? OH, NO NO! WHY HAVE A HUSBAND WHEN YOU CAN JUST SHACK UP WITH SOMEONE?
SHE COULD HAVE MARRIED KEVIN! BUT NO! KEVIN WASN'T EXCITING ENOUGH FOR HER!
© 2006 by NEA, Inc.
INSTEAD IT WAS: "HELLO, MA? I MET THIS NEAT GUY ON THE INTERNET!"
TIME FOR ME TO SIT BACK DOWN.
Peirce

MR. GALVIN? CAN I INTERVIEW YOU FOR THE SCHOOL NEWSPAPER?
I SUPPOSE SO.
OKAY, FIRST QUESTION: WHAT DO YOU THINK OF MS. LA CHANCE?
MS. LA CHANCE? SHE'S AN EXCELLENT TEACHER.
SO YOU LIKE HER!
YES, SHE'S A VERY NICE PERSON.
GOOD HEADLINE! "GALVIN LIKES LA CHANCE"!
WHAT? NO!
THAT MAKES IT SOUND LIKE THERE'S SOME KIND OF HANKY PANKY GOING ON!
OOOH! IS THERE?
OF COURSE NOT!!
10
15
SO YOU TWO KIDS DON'T HAVE A "RELATIONSHIP"?
NO! YOU'RE JUST MAKING STUFF UP!!
WINKA! WINKA!
THE NOTION THAT I HAVE A "RELATIONSHIP" WITH MS. LA CHANCE IS PURE FANTASY!!
OKAY, THANKS. I'VE GOT WHAT I NEED.
"GALVIN'S FANTASY: A RELATIONSHIP WITH LA CHANCE"
P.S. 38 WEEKLY BUGLE
IT'S AN EXCLUSIVE!
BUGLE
TIK TIK TIK
Peirce

CLASS, TODAY WE'RE STARTING SOMETHING NEW: BOOK BUDDIES!
BOOK BUDDIES?
WHAT'S BOOK BUDDIES?
MS. CLARKE
10/16
OOH! THAT'S WHERE WE HELP FIRST GRADERS WITH THEIR READING! RIGHT?
EXACTLY! EACH OF YOU WILL BE A "BUDDY" TO A FIRST GRADER!
OH HO! A CHANCE TO MOLD YOUNG MINDS!
YES, AND YOUR MIND'S GOT PLENTY OF MOLD TO GO AROUND!
TWO WORDS: "MINI ME"!
PEIRCE

ALL RIGHT, GANG, SETTLE DOWN! WE'RE ABOUT TO MEET OUR "BOOK BUDDIES"!
YAK YAK YAK YAK YAK
MRS. BIGBEE'S CLASS IS EXCITED TO MEET YOU ALL!
NOK! NOK!
MRS. BIGBEE? HEY, SHE WAS MY FIRST GRADE TEACHER!!
10/17
CHUCKLE! I WAS THE ONE WHO GAVE HER THE NICKNAME "MRS. BIG BUTT"!
© 2006 by NEA, Inc.
HEL-... ...OHHH NO.
I THOUGHT THE OLD GAL WOULD BE DEAD BY NOW!
Peirce

REMEMBER ME, MRS. BIGBEE? NATE WRIGHT?
HOW COULD I FORGET?
BOY, THE OL' CLASSROOM HASN'T CHANGED MUCH SINCE I WAS IN FIRST GRADE!...
OOP! THAT REMINDS ME!
GLUE
IS IT STILL HERE? IS IT... YES! IT IS!
© 2006 by NEA, Inc.
ARE YOU OKAY?
JUST HAVING A FEW FLASHBACKS.
GUYS, SEE THIS DENT? MY HEAD MADE THAT!
10/18
Peirce

ALL RIGHT, EVERYONE, PLEASE BE PATIENT AS WE PAIR EACH OF YOU WITH A "BOOK BUDDY"!
WHO AM **I** PAIRED WITH, MS. CLARKE?
I BELIEVE MRS. BIGBEE HAS SOMEONE IN MIND FOR YOU, NATE!
I DO INDEED, NATE! I'D LIKE YOU TO MEET...
PETER!
GAHH!
10/19
© 2006 by NEA, Inc.
AH! YOU TWO **KNOW** EACH OTHER!
UNFORTUNATELY, YESH. ISH THISH SHOME KIND OF SHICK JOKE?
Peirce

MRS. BIGBEE, SHURELY THERE MUSHT BE SHOME OTHER SHIXTH GRADER WHO'LL BE MY "BOOK BUDDY"!
I'M ALREADY FAMILIAR WITH THISH ONE!
YOU ARE, PETER? HOW?
I ATTENDED HISH LAME EXCUSHE FOR A SHUMMER CAMP!
PARDONE AY MWA, PETER, BUT "CAMP NATE" WAS NOT LAME!
10/20
© 2006 by NEA, Inc.
PLAYING "DUCK DUCK GOOSHE" WITH TWO PEOPLE ISHN'T LAME?
WELL, SURE IT IS, WITH THAT SORT OF ATTI-TUDE!
Peirce

OKAY, PETER, I'M YOUR "BOOK BUDDY"! LET'S GET STARTED!
DANA
NO!
DON'T WORRY, WE'LL START SLOW! HERE, LOOK! THE "BERENSTAIN BEARS"!
BOOK BOX!
10/21
NO!
TOO ADVANCED?
BOOK BOX!
NO!
HOW 'BOUT "PAT THE BUNNY"?
PEIRCE

MR. EUSTIS! WHAT ARE YOU DOING?
RAKING LEAVES, OBVIOUSLY!
BUT YOU ALWAYS HIRE **ME** TO DO THAT!
I KNOW, NATE, BUT THAT WAS BEFORE I WENT ON MY DIET! I HAD NO ENERGY, NO STAMINA!
NOW I'M FIT ENOUGH TO DO IT MY**SELF**!
SO LET ME GET THIS STRAIGHT: YOU LOST ALL THIS WEIGHT...
RIGHT...
10
22
YOU FEEL GREAT... YOU LOOK LIKE A MILLION BUCKS...
AHEM! WELL...
...AND YOU RE-WARD YOURSELF BY DOING **YARDWORK**?
ISN'T THERE A BETTER WAY OF CELEBRATING THE "NEW YOU"?
HI THERE.
Peirce

LISTEN, PETER, IF WE'RE GOING TO BE "BOOK BUDDIES", WE'D BETTER GET TO WORK!
BUT I DON'T **NEED** A "BOOK BUDDY"!
DON'T YOU WANT TO LEARN TO READ?
I ALREADY **KNOW** HOW TO READ! I'M A **PROLIFIC** READER!
I HAPPEN TO BE HALFWAY THROUGH JAMESH JOYCE'SH "**ULYSSHES**"!
UH... THAT'S COOL, PETER, BUT NEXT TIME YOU SAY "JAMES JOYCE'S ULYSSES", COULD YOU TURN YOUR HEAD IN THE OTHER DIRECTION?
10/23
Peirce

OKAY, PETER, YOU'RE RIGHT. YOU'RE AL-READY SUCH A GOOD READER, YOU DON'T REALLY NEED A BOOK BUDDY.
...BUT I'LL TELL YOU WHAT YOU DO NEED: A LITERARY ADVISOR!
LITERARY ADVISHOR?
SOMEONE TO EXPAND YOUR HORIZONS! SOME-ONE TO SHOW YOU THERE'S MORE TO LITERATURE THAN DUSTY OLD NOVELS!
FIVE SECONDS LATER...
SHE'S CALLED "FEMME FATALITY"!
COLOR ME SHMITTEN.
10/24
Peirce

WHAT IS GOING ON HERE?
JUST SOME PRODUCTIVE "BOOK BUDDY" TIME!
ARE YOU... SPUTTER!... HAVE YOU GOT PETER READING A COMIC BOOK??
YUP! "FEMME FATALITY" ISSUE #53!
10
25
NATE! THIS IS COMPLETELY INAPPROPRIATE!
YOU KNOW, YOU'RE RIGHT.
© 2006 by NEA, Inc.
NEXT WEEK I'LL BRING IN ISSUE #1 AND WE'LL START AT THE BEGINNING!
OOOH! SHWEET!
Peirce

I'LL TAKE THAT COMIC BOOK, BOYS!
HEY! MY "FEMME FATALITY"!
YOUR "FEMME FATALITY", NATE, IS EXPLOITATIVE TRASH!
NO, IT ISN'T! FEMME'S A GREAT CHAR-ACTER!
SHE'SH A SHTRONG WOMAN WHO SHTANDS UP FOR HERSHELF!
SHE'S A ROLE MODEL, MRS. BIGBEE! JUST LIKE YOU!
10/26
© 2006 by NEA, Inc.
EXCEPT THAT I'M NOT WEARING A SKIN-TIGHT TUBE TOP AND LEATH-ER MINI-SHORTS.
THANK HEAVENSH.
SSSH!
Peirce

DAD, DON'T YOU THINK YOU'D BETTER GET READY?
HMM? READY?
THE TRICK-OR-TREATERS WILL START SHOWING UP ANY MINUTE NOW!
TRICK-OR.... OH, MY..
DID YOU ACTUALLY BUY SOME DECENT CANDY THIS YEAR, I HOPE?
I... ER... WELL... UH...
DING DONG!
DON'T ANSWER THAT.
10/27
© 2006 by NEA, Inc.
Peirce

DING DONG!
DAD! CHOP CHOP! THERE'S TRICK-OR-TREATERS AT THE DOOR!
GULP
WE'VE GOT NOTHING TO GIVE THEM. I FORGOT TO BUY ANY TREATS.
DING DONG!
DING DONG! DING DONG! DING DONG!
DING DONG! DING DONG!
10/28
© 2006 by NEA, Inc.
BAM! BAM! BAM
BAM! BAM!
AM!
THIS ISN'T GOING TO BE PRETTY.
BAM!
Peirce

FAKE LEFT, THEN RUN A FADE TO THE RIGHT CORNER.
GOTCHA!
HIKE!
THINK YOU CAN COVER ME, FRANCIS? HA!
NOT WITH THIS BURST OF SPEED!
I'M OPEN!! I'M WIDE OPEN!!
10
29
GAAAA
TRIP!
YOU BEAT THE CORNERBACK, BUT YOU COULDN'T BEAT THE SAFETY!
NO, BUT I'M GOING TO SMASH HIM LATER.
PAT! PAT!

TRICK OR TREAT!
UH... HI, GUYS! WHAT'S UP?
"WHAT'S UP"? TRICK OR TREAT, THAT'S WHAT'S UP!
RIGHT! RIGHT! YUP! JUST... UH... HANG ON ONE SEC!
10/30
WE'LL HAVE SOME TREATS FOR YOU GUYS... WELL... UM... SHORTLY.
HURRY UP!
Peirce
© 2006 by NEA, Inc.

COME ON! ARE WE GETTING TREATS OR WHAT?
YES! YES! JUST WAIT ONE MINUTE!
HAPPY HALLOWEEN
DAD! MOVE IT! THESE KIDS ARE GETTING UGLY!
HERE!... *GASP!*... HERE'S ALL I COULD COME UP WITH!
HANG ON, GANG! HALLOWEEN TREATS COMIN' UP!
10/31
OKAY, WHO WANTS SOME BOUILLON CUBES?
GUYS?
GET THE EGGS, HUGHIE.
Peirce

NICE MOVE, DAD. ONLY YOU WOULD FORGET TO BUY HAL-LOWEEN CANDY!
IT WAS AN HONEST MISTAKE.
HONEST-SHMONEST! YOU'VE MADE US A TARGET FOR TICKED-OFF TRICK-OR-TREATERS! YOU MIGHT AS WELL HAVE SPRAY-PAINTED A BULLSEYE ON OUR HOUSE!
FSSSSHH!
NEVER MIND. THEY'RE DOING IT FOR YOU.
SIGH...
© 2006 by NEA, Inc.
peirce

MRS. GODFREY, HOW COME WE NEVER GET TREATS IN CLASS?
TREATS?
YEAH! BACK IN ELEMENTARY SCHOOL, WE GOT CANDY IF OUR BEHAVIOR WAS GOOD, OR IF WE DID WELL ON A TEST, OR...
SNORT! I DON'T BELIEVE IN TRYING TO MOTIVATE STUDENTS BY BRIBING THEM WITH FOOD.
TRANSLATION: SHE DOESN'T WANT TO SHARE ANY OF THE "JUNIOR MINTS" SHE'S GOT HIDDEN IN HER DESK.
11
2
Peirce

MRS. GODFREY? NATE'S ANNOYING ME.
NATE, STOP ANNOYING GINA.
OH YEAH? WELL, GINA IS ANNOYING **ME**!
BE QUIET, NATE, OR YOU'LL STAY AFTER SCHOOL.
11
3
WHAT? **WAIT** A MINUTE!
HOW COME WHEN **SHE**...?
MRS. GODFREY? NATE'S ANNOYING ME AGAIN.
NATE, STOP IT.
Peirce

MRS. GODFREY, HOW COME YOU NEVER YELL AT GINA?
I DON'T YELL.
OKAY, OKAY. HOW COME YOU NEVER **GET UPSET** WITH GINA?
WHY DO YOU THINK, NATE?
WHAT POSSIBLE REASON COULD I HAVE FOR **NEVER**, OVER THE COURSE OF **COUNTLESS** CLASS PERIODS, GETTING UP-SET WITH GINA??
11/4
I DUNNO... YOU'RE TOO BUSY YELLING AT **ME** ALL THE TIME?
I DON'T YELL!
Peirce

YEAH, WHAT IS IT?
MISTER, WOULD YOU LIKE TO BUY A WALL HANGING TO SUPPORT THE JUNIOR WOODCHUCKS?
NO. GOOD-BYE.
WAIT, WAIT! I HAVEN'T SHOWN YOU THE BROCHURE YET!
LOOK! THEY'VE ALL GOT SAYINGS ON THEM!
NOT INTERESTED.
"HONESTY IS THE BEST POLICY." THAT'S A GOOD ONE! OR HOW ABOUT "CARPE DIEM"? I THINK THAT'S FRENCH!
THIS ONE'S NICE: "WELCOME TO OUR HOME."
JUST ABOUT ANY SAYING YOU CAN THINK OF, I'VE GOT IT!
HOW ABOUT "BEWARE OF DOG"?
PEIRCE

ACCORDING TO THIS ARTICLE, WOMEN ARE ATTRACTED TO "BAD BOYS"!
COSMO
THERE'S SOMETHING ABOUT A REBEL THAT THE LADIES FIND IRRESISTIBLE!
HMMM!...
COSMO
11/6
GENTS, I DO BELIEVE I'M GETTING ANOTHER BRILLIANT IDEA!
"ANOTHER"?
YUP! THE HITS JUST KEEP ON COMIN'!
© 2006 by NEA, Inc.
Peirce

NATE! WHAT'S WITH THE GREASER LOOK?
JUST PART OF MY NEW "BAD BOY" IMAGE!
I GOT THE IDEA FROM THAT ARTICLE I READ ABOUT WOMEN BEING ATTRACTED TO REBELS!
11/7
POINK! POINK! POINK!
© 2006 by NEA, Inc.
YOUR HAIR IS CERTAINLY REBELLIOUS!
DANG! THERE GOES A WHOLE TUBE OF "DIPPITY-DO"!
POINK! POINK! POINK!
Peirce

A LEATHER JACKET?
HE'S A "BAD BOY".
11/8

YOU'RE ACTUALLY FOLLOWING THROUGH ON THAT DUMB IDEA?
DUMB IDEA? IT'S RIGHT HERE IN BLACK AND WHITE!

"FOR A MULTITUDE OF REASONS, WOMEN ARE OFTEN ATTRACTED TO "BAD BOYS"- MEN WHO SIMPLY AREN'T GOOD FOR THEM."

COSMO

THAT'S YOU, ALL RIGHT!
YEAH, YOU'RE GOOD FOR **NOTHING!**
HI, LADIES.
Peirce

JENNY! CHECK IT OUT! I'M A "BAD BOY"!
A WHAT?
A BAD BOY! I'M DANGEROUS, BABY! I'M BAD TO THE BONE!
YOU?
HA HA HA HA
HA HA HA HA HA
HA HA HA HA
I'M HAVING TROUBLE GETTING MY BADNESS ACROSS.
WELL, THERE'S A DIF-FERENCE BETWEEN "BAD" AND "LAME."
PEIRCE
11/9
© 2006 by NEA, Inc.

WHAT'S UP, LADIES?
UH... NOTHING.
HEY! WE DIDN'T INVITE YOU TO SIT WITH US!
INVITE ME? LISTEN, I'M A "BAD BOY"!
I SIT WHEREVER I WANT TO SIT!
...AND RIGHT ABOUT NOW, THE COT IN THE NURSE'S OFFICE SOUNDS PRETTY GOOD.
© 2006 by NEA, Inc.
11/10
Peirce

UH... NATE?
YUP?
WHY ARE YOU WEARING A LEATHER JACKET OVER YOUR SMOCK?
BECAUSE I'M A BAD BOY!
YOU'RE A BAD BOY?
CORRECT!
© 2006 by NEA, Inc.
SON, I HAVEN'T SEEN A LESS CONVINCING "BAD" SINCE MICHAEL JACKSON.
WHO?
Peirce

CHESS MEET
VS.
JEFFERSON
TODAY
3:30
ETERIA
I CAN'T BELIEVE YOU'RE THE NUMBER TWO PLAYER ON YOUR TEAM!
ON OUR TEAM YOU'D BE NO BETTER THAN NUMBER SIX! MAYBE SEVEN!
11/12
THERE! SEE? YOU JUST PROVED MY POINT! YOU WALKED RIGHT INTO MY TRAP!
CHECK! WHAT DO YOU SAY TO THAT?
HERE.
A FORK?
IT SHOULD COME IN HANDY...
...WHEN YOU EAT A BIG OL' SLICE OF HUMBLE PIE.
CHECKMATE.
GAWK!
BON APPÉTIT!
Peirce

REMEMBER THAT SUB WE HAD LAST SPRING?
MRS. ESTERHAUS!
OH, YEAH! WAS **SHE** IN OVER HER HEAD!
FOR THREE DAYS WE DID NOTHING IN CLASS BUT PLAY "HANGMAN"! IT WAS **GREAT!**
THINK WE COULD GET HER BACK?
WELL, MAYBE. IF ONE OF THE **REAL** TEACHERS GOT SICK OR SOMETHING.
HMMM... RIGHT...
11/13
© 2006 by NEA, Inc.
...AND BY THE WAY, THAT WAS JUST A STATEMENT OF FACT, NOT A...
FIRST, WE'LL NEED A DART GUN.
Peirce

GUYS! OUR WISH CAME TRUE! I JUST HEARD MRS. GODFREY IS SICK TODAY!
YESSS!
WHO'S THE SUB? IS IT MRS. ESTERHAUS?
I'M NOT SURE! I HOPE SO!
HEY, EVEN IF IT'S NOT MRS. ESTERHAUS, WHO CARES? ANY SUB IS GOING TO BE A DAY TRIP TO FUN CITY!
11
14
AWRIGHT, SCRUBS! SIDDOWN AND PACK IT!
COACH JOHN!
Peirce

COACH JOHN! WHAT ARE YOU DOING HERE?
WHAT DOES IT LOOK LIKE, SOLDIER? SUBSTITUTE TEACHING!
BUT YOU'RE A GYM TEACHER!
WHOA, SON! I CAN TEACH ANYTHING!
I'M AS COMFORTABLE IN A CLASSROOM AS I AM IN A LOCKER ROOM! I'M NOT JUST AN ATHLETE!
11/15
HE'S NOT JUST AN ATHLETE.
NOW DROP AND GIVE ME TWENTY!!
Peirce

OOH! WHO'S THE SUB?
YOU DON'T KNOW? GINA, THAT'S COACH JOHN!!
WHO'S COACH JOHN?
HE'S A PSYCHO, THAT'S WHO! HE'S A TOTAL DISCIPLINE FREAK!
WELL, GOOD! THIS CLASS COULD USE A LITTLE DISCI-
HEY! NO TALKING IN RANKS, BLONDIE!
11/16
© 2006 by NEA, Inc.
"BLONDIE"?
YOU WERE SAYING?
YOU TOO, CACTUS HEAD!
Peirce

YOU THERE! STOP YOUR YACKING!
YOU REMIND ME OF A KID I COACHED AT SOCCER CAMP LAST YEAR! YOU'RE JUST LIKE HIM: A SPIKY-HAIRED CHATTERBOX!
11/17
I REMEMBER HE PLAYED GOALIE, AND ONE DAY...
COACH JOHN! THAT WAS ME!
© 2006 by NEA, Inc.
Peirce
SEE? BACKTALK! GAD, YOU'RE LIKE HIS TWIN!
THIS GUY'S A FEW SLICES SHORT OF A LOAF.

ALL RIGHT, SOLDIER, YOUR CONSTANT CHATTERING IS DISRUPTING MY CLASS! YOU GIVE ME NO CHOICE BUT TO RESPOND!
SO... YOU'RE SENDING ME TO DETEN-TION?
DETENTION? SO YOU CAN SIT AROUND FILING YOUR NAILS? I THINK NOT!
MY STYLE OF DISCIPLINE IS A BIT MORE FORCEFUL!
11/18
© 2006 by NEA, Inc.
I'VE NEVER RUN WIND SPRINTS IN THE SOCIAL STUDIES ROOM BEFORE.
PICK 'EM UP AND PUT 'EM DOWN!
Peirce

SHEILA? WE HAVE A NEW STUDENT! MEET BECKY!
HI!
WILL YOU SHOW HER AROUND THE SCHOOL?
SURE! C'MON, BECKY!
11/19
THIS IS SMALLER THAN MY OLD SCHOOL!
YUP! WE'RE PRETTY TINY!
...BUT THAT'S NICE, BECAUSE YOU GET TO **KNOW** EVERY-ONE!
I KNOW EVERY SINGLE KID IN THE SIXTH GRADE **PERSONALLY!**
WOW!
WHO WAS THAT?
I HAVE NO IDEA.
Peirce

PSST! NATE! CAN I BORROW YOUR ERASER?
HERE.
WHOA! WHOA! WHOA!
WHAT WAS THAT? WHAT DO YOU CALL THAT??
OH... UH...
I... UM... THREW A PENCIL.
YOU THREW IT UNDER-HAND!! LIKE MY AUNT ALICE!!
11/20
© 2006 by NEA, Inc.
PEIRCE
BRING IT OVER THE TOP! AND FOLLOW THROUGH!
THIS IS SURREAL.

COACH JOHN IS THE PITS! I'M BAILING!
COACH JOHN, I'M SICK. CAN I GO TO THE NURSE'S OFFICE?
SICK, EH?
11/21
BOO!
© 2006 by NEA, Inc.
YOU'RE FINE. SIT DOWN.
FORGET THE NURSE, I NEED A BATH-ROOM.
Peirce

I NOTICE A FEW OF YOU SCHOLARS ARE TRYING TO GET EXCUSED FROM CLASS BECAUSE YOU'RE "SICK"!
WELL, YOU DON'T EVEN KNOW WHAT SICK IS, SOLDIERS! YOU HAVE NO EARTHLY IDEA!
11/22
YOU WANT TO TALK SICK? TRY EATING A JAR OF RANCID MAYONNAISE AND THEN WATCHING "THE EXORCIST"!
NOW I REALLY DO NEED TO BE EXCUSED.
BUT ENOUGH "PLEDGE WEEK" STORIES...
Peirce

COACH JOHN IS THE WORST SUBSTITUTE TEACHER EVER! IT'S LIKE HAVING SOCIAL STUDIES WITH GENGHIS KHAN!
11
23
I THINK I MIGHT ACTUALLY PREFER MRS. GODFR–..
WAIT! DON'T SAY IT!
BUT IT'S TRUE!
NO! BITE YOUR TONGUE!
I CAN'T HELP IT!
© 2006 by NEA, Inc.
GET A– HOLD OF YOURSELF!
WHAT THE..?
NO!
SLAP
SLAP
SLAP
SLAP
SLAP
Peirce

COACH JOHN IS AN ABSOLUTE PSYCHO! I DON'T THINK I CAN STAND ANOTHER DAY OF HIM SUBBING!
YOU WON'T HAVE TO!
I JUST SAW MRS. GODFREY! SHE'S BACK!
SHE IS?
11
24
© 2006 by NEA, Inc.
peirce

BOY, AM I GLAD YOU'RE BACK, MRS. GODFREY! COACH JOHN WAS THE WORST SUB WE'VE EVER **HAD**!
HOW NICE TO BE MISSED.
I SEE IN COACH JOHN'S CLASS NOTES THAT YOU FAILED TO COMPLETE THE WORKSHEETS ON MONDAY AND TUESDAY.
WELL, YEAH, BUT THAT WAS BECAUSE...
PASS THEM IN BY THE END OF THE DAY OR YOU'LL HAVE DETENTION FOR A WEEK.
OH, HOW I HATE HER.
11/25
© 2006 by NEA, Inc.
Peirce

OKAY, CARLOS AND NATE! STEP UP TO THE LINE, GENTS!
LOOSE-BALL DRILL! READY... SET...
GO!
GRUNT!
PANT! GASP!
TRIP!
SKWEEEEEE!!
!
WORST FLOOR BURN I'VE EVER SEEN.
CAN WE DO AWAY WITH THE "SHIRTS VS. SKINS" THING?

DAD, CAN I HAVE A FEW BUCKS TO BUY HOT LUNCH?
NOT TODAY, NATE.
11/27
WE'VE GOT TO WORK OUR WAY THROUGH THESE THANKSGIVING LEFTOVERS!
EAT HEARTY.
Peirce
© 2006 by NEA, Inc.
HEARTY HAR HAR.
PLEASE TELL ME THAT'S CRAN-BERRY SAUCE.
SCHOO
BUS

GAH! MY DAD PACKED ME TURKEY AGAIN!
JEFF! WANNA TRADE LUNCHES?
ALL I'VE GOT IS THANKSGIVING LEFTOVERS.
11
28
ME TOO, BUT WE CAN...
LIVER PATÉ ON CABBAGE LEAVES, CHILLED OYSTER SOUP, TOFU KABOBS, AND A THERMOS OF PRUNE JUICE.
© 2006 by NEA, Inc.
REMIND ME NOT TO ATTEND ANY HOLIDAY PARTIES AT JEFF'S HOUSE.
PEIRCE

ARRRGH! MY DAD PACKED ME TURKEY AGAIN!
11/29
I DON'T EVEN LIKE TURKEY THAT MUCH, AND HE'S MAKING ME EAT IT SIX DAYS IN A ROW!
SIX DAYS IN A ROW!
SIX DAYS IN A...
POST-THANKSGIVING STRESS DISORDER.
Peirce

TEDDY! WANNA SWAP LUNCHES?
SURE!
YES! GOOD! HERE YOU GO! DONE DEAL! NO "TAKE BACKS"!
ZIP!
ZWIP!
HA! FINALLY I GET TO EAT SOMETHING OTHER THAN...
...TURKEY?
TURKEY **SALAD**. WELCOME TO MY NIGHT-MARE.
11 30
Peirce

DAD, NO TURKEY FOR LUNCH TODAY! I'M DONE WITH TURKEY!
NO TURKEY?
NO TURKEY DRUM-STICKS?
NO!
NO TURKEY SANDWICHES?
NO!
NO TURKEY SALAD?
NO!
12/1
© 2006 by NEA, Inc.
NO MOUTH-WATERING CHOCOLATE CHIP TURKOOKIES?
NO!
Peirce

I DON'T THINK I'LL EAT TURKEY AGAIN AS LONG AS I LIVE!
BY MAKING ME EAT SO MUCH OF IT, MY DAD HAS RUINED A PERFECTLY GOOD FOOD FOR ME!
12/2
I ONCE THREW UP AFTER EATING A BUNCH OF GUMMI BEARS AND NOW I, LIKE, TOTALLY HATE GUMMI BEARS.
THANKS, TEDDY. WHAT A FASCINATING ADDITION TO THE DISCUSSION.
ONE BEAR CAME OUT MY NOSE.
© 2006 by NEA, Inc.
Peirce

I'M IN THE ZONE TODAY! I'M IN THE ZONE!
WHERE'S THE ZONE?
IT'S NOT A PLACE! IT'S MORE LIKE A FEELING!
12/3
IT'S THE FEELING YOU CAN DO NO WRONG! LIKE, IN BASKETBALL, IT'S THE FEELING YOU CAN'T MISS A SHOT!
...AND YOU REALLY CAN'T MISS! NOT WHEN YOU'RE IN THE ZONE!
HOW DO YOU GET IN THE ZONE?
IT JUST HAPPENS! ALL OF A SUDDEN IT'S JUST THERE!
FOO!
THUD!
OW!
...AND THEN, JUST AS SUDDENLY, IT'S GONE.
WHO THREW THAT?
COACH
Peirce

GOOD MORN–
DIBS.
HUH?
I CALLED DIBS.
12/4
ON WHAT?
ON EVERY-THING. FOREVER.
RICK 7
B
WAIT A MINUTE!
YOU'RE IN MY SEAT.
Peirce
© 2006 by NEA, Inc.

LISTEN, YOU CAN'T CALL DIBS ON **EVERY-THING**!
I JUST DID.
I CALLED DIBS IN PERPETUITY ON EVERYTHING IN THE UNIVERSE.
IN THE **UNIVERSE**?
12/5
NATE, THAT'S **RIDICULOUS**! THE WHOLE **UNIVERSE**?
OKAY, OKAY. MAYBE THE WHOLE UNIVERSE **IS** A BIT MUCH.
© 2006 by NEA, Inc.
DIBS ON EVERYTHING IN THE SOLAR SYSTEM.
MUCH BETTER.
Peirce

NO, YOU CAN'T! IT'S JUST SO STUPID!
I ALREADY DID!
HEY, SHUT UP, SCRUB!
GENTS, GENTS! WHAT'S THE PROB?
NATE CALLED DIBS ON EVERYTHING! YOU JUST CAN'T DO THAT!
YOU'RE JUST MAD 'CAUSE I BEAT YOU TO IT!
HE'S RIGHT, NATE, YOU CAN'T DO THAT.
12/6
... BECAUSE I CALLED DIBS ON EVERYTHING YESTERDAY!
YOU'VE BEEN OUT-DIBBED!
WHAT? HOLD IT! WITNESSES! I WANT WITNESSES!
Peirce

DIBS ON THAT BROWNIE!
WHAT? THAT'S MY BROWNIE!
YOU JUST STOLE MY BROWNIE!
I DIDN'T STEAL IT! I CALLED IT!
BUT IT ALREADY BELONGED TO ME!
OH, REALLY? DID YOU CALL IT?
12/7
© 2006 by NEA, Inc.
I DIDN'T HAVE TO CALL IT!
EW. WALNUTS.
Peirce

SOMEONE LEFT A PEN HERE.
OOH! DIBS!
HEY, THAT BELONGS TO SOME-ONE!
YEAH! TO ME! I CALLED DIBS ON IT, SO ACCORDING TO DIBS LAW, IT NOW BELONGS TO ME!
12/8
THAT'S MY PEN.
!
© 2006 by NEA, Inc.
THERE'S DIBS LAW, AND THEN THERE'S A HIGHER AUTHORITY!
Peirce

DIBS ON JENNY!
WHAT WAS THAT? DIBS ON ME?
RIGHT! JUST IN CASE TEDDY WAS THINKING OF ASKING YOU OUT, I CALLED DIBS ON YOU!
YOU CAN'T CALL DIBS ON A PERSON!
POW!
© 2006 by NEA, Inc.
...UNLESS IT'S THE SCHOOL NURSE!
I LOVE HER FIERY SPIRIT.
12/9
Peirce

FLIP!
PLUP!
CHK!
FLIP!
PLUP!
CHK!
FLIP!
12/10
PLUP!
CHK!
FLIP!
TRUE/FALSE TEST.

HISTORY IS FILLED WITH PEOPLE WHO'VE ACCOMPLISHED GREAT THINGS WITHOUT ANY FORMAL SCHOOLING, RIGHT?
RIGHT.
SO I SHOULD BE ABLE TO ACCOMPLISH GREAT THINGS WITHOUT ANY FORMAL SCHOOLING!
IN THEORY.
COOL. HAVE A NICE LIFE.
An education is a privilege. An education is a privilege. An
THIS IS EVEN MORE FORMAL THAN USUAL.
KEEP WRITING.
12/11
Peirce

MR. GALVIN, I MISUNDERSTOOD YOU WHEN YOU TOLD ME TO WRITE A REPORT ON PLUTO.
PLEASE DON'T TELL ME YOU WROTE ABOUT THE DISNEY CHARACTER.
NO, NO! OF COURSE NOT!
I WROTE ABOUT THAT FAT GUY WHO'S ALWAYS TRYING TO BEAT UP POPEYE.
12/12
© 2006 by NEA, Inc.
Peirce
THAT'S "BLUTO," SON.
WAIT, WASN'T HE ALSO SOMETIMES CALLED "BRUTUS"?
THERE! SEE? NO WONDER I WAS CONFUSED!

MRS. GODFREY, CAN I BE EXCUSED FROM CLASS? MY NOSE IS BLEEDING.
LET ME SEE.
MRS. GODF
LET YOU SEE?
LET ME SEE.
ZWIP!
12/13
© 2006 by NEA, Inc.
I CLOT QUICKLY.
DETENTION.
Peirce

MRS. CZERWICKI, WHAT SORT OF MESSAGE ARE TEACHERS SENDING WHEN THEY DON'T TRUST US STUDENTS?
DETENTION ROOM
IET, PLEASE
I ASKED TO BE EXCUSED FROM SOCIAL STUDIES BECAUSE I HAD A BLOODY NOSE, AND MRS. GODFREY DIDN'T BELIEVE ME!
AND DID YOU HAVE A BLOODY NOSE?
NO, I WAS JUST TRYING TO GET OUT OF CLASS.
BUT THE POINT IS, WHERE IS THE TRUST?
SIT DOWN, CHILD.
© 2006 by NEA, Inc.
12/14
Peirce

WOW! COOL DRAWING!
I'VE BEEN WORKING ON IT ALL PERIOD!
THIS MAY VERY WELL BE THE BEST PIECE OF ART I'VE EVER MADE!
12/15
UNFORTUNATELY, YOU MADE IT DURING SOCIAL STUDIES.
...KOFF!... ...WHICH IS WHY IT'S A PICTURE OF THE GETTYSBURG ADDRESS!
WITH NINJAS?
Peirce

HERE'S WHAT I DON'T GET, MRS. GODFREY: HOW AM I SUPPOSED TO PAY ATTENTION IN CLASS...
...WHEN YOU KEEP SENDING ME TO THE PRINCIPAL'S OFFICE DURING CLASS? YOU'RE NOT MAKING SENSE!
I'M A TEACHER. I DON'T HAVE TO MAKE SENSE.
© 2006 by NEA, Inc.
NCIPAL
ODDLY ENOUGH, EVERYTHING HAS JUST BECOME CRYSTAL CLEAR.
12/16
Peirce

RRRRINNNNGG!
THERE'S THE BELL.
JINX!
JINX! JINX! JINX! JINX!
OWE ME A COKE!
12/17
OWE ME A COKE! OWE ME A COKE! OWE ME A COKE! OWE ME A COKE!
FOOOO!..
GASP!
PANT
PANT PANT
WHEEZE
WHO WON?
IT WAS A TIE.
JINX!
SIGH..
PEIRCE

I'M MAKING A LIST OF ALL THE UNFAIR ADVANTAGES TEACHERS HAVE OVER STUDENTS, MR. ROSA!
HM.
ITEM ONE: YOU GET TO USE AN ELECTRIC PENCIL SHARPENER WHILE WE USE THIS CRANK MODEL! THIS THING IS A TOTAL DINOSAUR!
I MEAN, YOU MIGHT AS WELL JUST MAKE US WHITTLE OUR PENCILS!
12/18
© 2006 by NEA, Inc.
GREAT IDEA. STUDENTS WITH KNIVES.
THERE'S ITEM TWO: YOU GUYS GET TO USE SARCASM!
Peirce

HERE'S ANOTHER INJUSTICE: YOU TEACHERS HAVE YOUR OWN LOUNGE TO HANG OUT IN! WE KIDS GET NOTHING!
WHERE ARE WE SUPPOSED TO HANG OUT?
"ARE THERE NO PRISONS? ARE THERE NO WORKHOUSES?"
THE HOLIDAYS DO STRANGE THINGS TO PEOPLE.
© 2006 by NEA, Inc.
12/19
Peirce

HERE'S ANOTHER THING THAT'S NOT FAIR: WE STUDENTS GET NOTHING FOR BEING HERE! YOU TEACHERS GET PAID!
"PAID."
HEH HEH... WE GET "PAID." HEH HA HA...
HA HA HA HA HA HA
WE'RE ROLLING IN IT!
HA HA HA
HA HA HA
HA HA
12/20
© 2006 by NEA, Inc.
HA HA HA HA HA H
I'M RICH!
HA
HA HA HA
HA
THEY ALL ACT THIS WAY WHEN ANYONE MENTIONS MONEY.
Peirce

DAD, HOW ABOUT GETTING ME A DOG FOR CHRIST-MAS?
NOPE. SORRY, NATE.
CL
WE'VE DISCUSSED THIS BEFORE, AND I'VE TOLD YOU WE...
OKAY, OKAY. YOU DON'T HAVE TO GET ME A DOG.
CLASSIFIED
SPORTS
I'LL GET **YOU** A DOG.
FINE.
12/21
© 2006 by NEA, Inc.
WAIT... WHAT?
NO!
...AND REMEMBER, IT'S THE **THOUGHT** THAT COUNTS!
Peirce

I DON'T GET IT, DAD. WHAT'S YOUR PROBLEM WITH GETTING A DOG?
HOW ABOUT ALL THE **SHEDDING**?
SPORT
I DON'T WANT TO SPEND THE REST OF MY LIFE SWEEPING UP **DOG HAIR**!
THE REST OF YOUR **LIFE**? ISN'T THAT A BIT **DRAMATIC**?
12/22
DOGS LIVE ABOUT TWELVE YEARS! THAT HARDLY BRINGS YOU TO THE END OF YOUR...
ACTUALLY, YOU'RE ALREADY PRETTY OLD, SO MAYBE...
GO PLAY OUTSIDE, BOY.
SPORTS
Peirce

YOU DON'T WANT TO GET A DOG BECAUSE THEY **SHED**, RIGHT? WELL, I'VE BEEN RE-SEARCHING DOGS THAT **DON'T** SHED!
HOW ABOUT ONE OF THESE POODLE MIXES? WE COULD GET A LABRADOODLE! OR A SCHNOODLE!
HOW ABOUT A WESTIEPOO? WE COULD GET A WESTIEPOO!
12/23
© 2006 by NEA, Inc.
IF I EVER GOT A DOG CALLED A "WESTIEPOO," I'D BE DRUMMED OUT OF MY THURSDAY NIGHT POKER GAME.
Peirce

'Twas the night before Christmas
When all through the house,
Not a creature was stirring
FTS
OPEN LATE XMAS EVE
12 24
TIES
CLEARANCE
$
Not even a mouse.
PHEW!

"TO NATE, FROM DAD"! HMM, WHAT COULD THIS BE?
WHA...? IT'S... IS THIS A COLLAR? IT'S A COLLAR!
IT'S A BELT.
YOU GOT ME A COLLAR! WHICH MEANS YOU ALSO GOT ME A DOG!
IT'S A BELT.
HERE, BOY!!
IT'S A BELT.
12/25
© 2006 by NEA, Inc.
Peirce

IT WOULD HAVE BEEN NICE TO HAVE SNOW FOR CHRIST-MAS.
YEAH, IT WOULD BE LESS PAINFUL.
12 26
WHAT DO YOU MEAN, LESS PAINF—...?
© 2006 by NEA, Inc.
WHAM!
OH.
SPITSY, YOU IDIOT.
PANT PANT
PANT PANT
Peirce

HEY! A SNOW-FLAKE!
WHAT? NO!
DON'T YOU WANT IT TO SNOW?
NOT NOW! NOT DURING VACATION!
IT'S SUPPOSED TO SNOW DURING SCHOOL! THEN IT'S A SNOW DAY AND WE GET TO STAY HOME! THIS IS A TOTAL WASTE OF A SNOWSTORM!
12/27
© 2006 by NEA, Inc.
PEIRCE
WHO DOES ONE COM-PLAIN TO ABOUT MISTIMED WEATHER EVENTS?
HELLO, CAN I SPEAK TO CHIEF METEOR-OLOGIST WINK SUMMERS?

HI, IS THIS CHIEF METEOROLOGIST WINK SUMMERS?... WINK! NATE WRIGHT, HERE!
LISTEN, WINK, WHAT'S UP WITH THIS SNOW? WE DON'T NEED THIS NOW, WE NEED IT NEXT WEEK! WHEN WE'RE BACK IN SCHOOL!
WHAT?... YOU DON'T CONTROL THE WEATH-ER? OH, REALLY? GEE, I WASN'T AWARE OF THAT!
12/28
OH, DID I SOUND SARCASTIC? SOR-RY!
I NEVER THOUGHT I'D FEEL SORRY FOR A TV WEATHERMAN.
Peirce

LISTEN, WINK, SINCE I'VE GOT YOU ON THE PHONE, LET ME GIVE YOU SOME FEEDBACK ON LAST NIGHT'S FORECAST.

THAT BLUE BLAZER WASN'T REALLY DOING YOU ANY FAVORS, DUDE. IT MADE YOU LOOK A LITTLE PUDGY.

THEN AGAIN, YOU **ARE** A LITTLE PUDGY, WINK. I MEAN, YOU REALLY PACKED ON THE POUNDS AFTER THAT BABE WHO DOES THE MOVIE REVIEWS DUMPED YOU.
12/29

YOU'RE BETTER OFF WITHOUT HER, MAN. SHE ONLY GAVE **ONE STAR** TO "SNAKES ON A PLANE"!
HANG UP, WINK!
PEIRCE

HOW COME YOU'RE ALWAYS CALLING THAT TV WEATHER GUY?
YEAH, YOU'RE OBSESSED WITH HIM!
YOU KNOW EVERYTHING ABOUT THE GUY!
LOOK, I JUST HAPPEN TO BE A FAN OF HIS WORK, THAT'S ALL!
...AND I DON'T "KNOW EVERYTHING ABOUT THE GUY"!
BOOP BEEP BEEP BOOP BEEP BOOP BOOP
12/30
© 2006 by NEA, Inc.
HELLO, WINK? IT'S TIME TO PICK UP YOUR SON FROM HIS OBOE LESSON.
Peirce

WHAT ARE YOU EATING, FRANCIS?
A PEANUT BUTTER AND POTATO CHIP SAND-WICH.
CRUNCH!
WHAT A GREAT IDEA!
YUP! I'VE BEEN DOING IT FOR YEARS!
WHOA! WHOA, BOY!
WHAT?
DON'T MAKE IT SOUND LIKE YOU INVENTED THE PEANUT BUTTER AND POTATO CHIP SANDWICH! I CAME UP WITH THAT IDEA!
12/31
YOU DID?
YES! BACK IN, LIKE, SECOND GRADE!
WHATEVER.
NO! NO, NOT "WHAT-EVER"! I WANT MY CREDIT!
I WANT THE WORLD TO KNOW JUST WHO INVENTED THE PEANUT BUTTER AND POTATO CHIP SANDWICH!
I STARTED EATING THEM BACK IN 1957!
FORGET EVERYTHING I JUST SAID.
I ALWAYS DO.
CRUNCH!
Peirce

CHESTER! MY MAN!
WHY DO YOU ALWAYS DO THAT?
DO WHAT?
CALL ME YOUR MAN. I'M NOT YOUR MAN.
IT MAKES ME MAD.
IT'S JUST... I'M BEING NICE, DUDE! I'M BEING FRIENDLY!
WHEN YOU CALL ME "DUDE", IT MAKES ME WANT TO HIT YOU IN THE FACE.
I'LL JUST GO STAND OVER HERE.
1-1-07
© 2007 by NEA, Inc.
Peirce

HOW MUCH DO YOU THINK CHESTER WEIGHS?
HMM... I'D SAY ABOUT...
CHOMP!
CRUNCH! CHOMPF! NARF! NARGH!
BURRP!
ABOUT FIVE POUNDS MORE THAN HE DID A SECOND AGO.
DID HE JUST EAT AN ENTIRE CHICK-EN?
BONES AND ALL.
1/2/07
Peirce

I'M GOING TO ASK CHESTER HOW MUCH HE WEIGHS.
WHAT? WHY?
I'M JUST CURIOUS, THAT'S ALL.
DON'T DO IT, NATE! HE'S TOUCHY ABOUT HIS WEIGHT! HE'S VERY SENSITIVE!
WUMP!
SENSITIVE, YET FRIGHTENINGLY VIOLENT.
I'LL GO SEE IF THE JANITOR HAS A "JAWS OF LIFE."
1-3-07
© 2007 by NEA, Inc.
Peirce

CHESTER IS HUGE. HE'S AN ABSOLUTE HOUSE OUT THERE!
HOUSE? HE'S A DUPLEX!
CHUCKLE HE'S A CASTLE!
ME, I'M YOUR BASIC DUTCH COLONIAL!
NO, YOU'RE TOO SMALL TO BE A DUTCH COLONIAL.
YOU'RE LIKE A CAPE.
1/4/07
A CAPE? I DON'T THINK I'M A CAPE...
HOW 'BOUT A BUNGALOW?
I KNOW! A TRAILER!
© 2007 by NEA, Inc.
WITH VINYL SIDING!
COACH, WHAT KIND OF HOUSE AM I?
I HAVE A HEADACHE.
Peirce

YES! CHESTER!
WAY TO TAKE IT TO THE HOOP, BIG GUY!
1/5/07
BOOMP!
NEVER TRY TO BUMP CHESTS WITH A GUY WHO'S 6'6," THREE BILLS.
MEDIC.
Peirce

PASS ME THE BALL.
NO, CHESTER! NOT AT MIDCOURT!
COACH WANTS YOU TO SCORE DOWN LOW, NOT HANDLE THE BALL IN THE OPEN FLOOR!
PASS ME THE BALL, OR I'LL TEAR YOUR HEAD OFF AND DRIBBLE IT DOWN THE LANE.
1-6-07
© 2007 by NEA, Inc.
OUR COMMUNI-CATION IS REALLY IMPROVING OUT THERE.
Peirce

WHAT'S WITH THE BLIND-FOLD?
WE'RE TESTING NATE!
HE CLAIMS HE CAN IDENTIFY ANY FOOD STRICTLY BY SMELL!
SNIFF! TUNA ON WHOLE WHEAT, WITH A SLICE OF TOMATO!
HE GOT IT!
SNIFF! HAM, SWISS, AND LETTUCE ON A SESAME BULKY ROLL...
1/7/07
WOW!
...WITH JUST A SMIDGE OF HONEY MUSTARD!
HERE! TRY THIS!
SNIFF!
GAG!
THIS... (KOFF!)... THIS IS FOUL!
OOLP! I HAVE NO IDEA.
ARE YOU SURE THIS IS EVEN FOOD?
THAT QUESTION HAS BEEN ASKED MANY TIMES.
THIS IS WHY I NEVER BUY HOT LUNCH.
SPLUT!
TODAY: CASSEROLE
Peirce

WHAT THE...? HEY! I'VE BEEN ROBBED!
ROBBED?
I HAD MONEY IN HERE FOR THE BOOK FAIR, AND NOW IT'S GONE!
OH HO! THIS SOUNDS LIKE A JOB FOR...
1/8
...NATE WRIGHT, PRIVATE EYE!!
Peirce
© 2007 by NEA, Inc.
WAY TO MAIN-TAIN A LOW PROFILE.
SHALL WE DISCUSS MY FEE?
?
?
?

SO YOU'RE GOING TO HELP ME FIND MY MISSING MONEY?
EXACTLY, FRANCIS! NATE WRIGHT, PRIVATE EYE, IS ON THE CASE!
1/9
WHAT'S THE FIRST STEP? REPORT IT TO THE PRINCIPAL?
NO, NO, NO...
THE FIRST STEP IS TO CHANGE INTO MY **SLEUTHING CLOTHES!**
© 2007 by NEA, Inc.
SECOND STEP: I'LL ACT LIKE I DON'T KNOW YOU.
JOLLY GOOD.
Peirce

WHO ARE YOU SUPPOSED TO BE, SHERLOCK HOLMES?
I CAN BE ANYONE, DEAR BOY.
SPANIS CLUB Fies THURS FEB.
LIKE ALL GREAT DETECTIVES, I AM A CHAMELEON! I CAN CHANGE MY IDENTITY AT WILL!
1 10
I'VE MASTERED THE ART OF ADAPTING TO MY SURROUNDINGS, SO THAT I'M SCARCELY NOTICED!
F
© 2007 by NEA, Inc.
I CAN BECOME ALMOST INVISIBLE.
HEY, WHO'S THE LOSER IN THE CAPE?
HA HA HA HA HA HA HA HA HA
Peirce

ALL RIGHT, FRANCIS, LET'S DISCUSS THE FACTS. HOW MUCH MONEY IS MISSING?
TWENTY BUCKS.
TWENTY DOLLARS. HMMM... AND NOW THAT MONEY HAS MYSTERIOUSLY DIS-APPEARED, EH WHAT?
RIGHT.
HOW DO WE KNOW **YOU** DIDN'T TAKE IT?
WHAT? IT'S **MY MONEY**! WHY WOULD I STEAL FROM MY-**SELF**?
THE DEVIANT MIND IS OFTEN DIFFICULT TO UNDER-STAND.
... SAID THE KID WEAR-ING A SHERLOCK HOLMES COSTUME AND SMOK-ING A BUBBLE PIPE.
1/11
Peirce

FRANCIS! I HEARD YOU HAD SOME MONEY STOLEN!
NEVER FEAR, SHEILA! THE CULPRIT **WILL** BE CAUGHT!
I'M CURRENTLY CONDUCTING AN EXHAUSTIVE INVESTIGATION OF FRANCIS' LOCKER, WHICH WILL UNDOUBTEDLY YIELD A **MULTITUDE** OF VITAL INFORMATION!
GIRL POWER!
NICK!
1/12
UH... THAT'S **MY** LOCKER.
© 2007 by NEA, Inc.
FOR A DETECTIVE, HE'S SURPRISINGLY CLUELESS.
OH, I'M NOT SURPRISED.
HI.
Peirce

JENNY, M'LADY!
WHAT'S UP, DORKUS?
MERELY A LITTLE SLEUTHING, MY DEAR! OUR FRIEND FRANCIS HAD SOME MONEY STOLEN FROM HIS LOCKER THIS MORNING!
MAY I ASK YOU A FEW QUESTIONS?
WHAT-EVER.
1/13
© 2007 by NEA, Inc.
DO YOU FIND MEN IN CAPES SEXY?
CRIPES.
Peirce

GO, SPITSY! GO!
WURF!
WHAT'S UP?
SPITSY IS UN-LOCKING THE PREDATOR WITHIN!
WHADDA YA MEAN?
TEDDY, WHAT'S THE NATURAL ENEMY OF DOGS? DUH! IT'S CATS!
WELL, EARLIER I SAW A CAT IN THE VACANT LOT! SO I SENT SPITSY IN THAT DIRECTION!
1/14
YOU THINK HE'LL TRACK IT DOWN?
OF COURSE HE WILL! HIS NATURAL CANINE IN-STINCTS WILL KICK IN!
BELIEVE YOU ME, SPITSY WILL FIND THAT CAT!
!
WHEN YOU'RE RIGHT, YOU'RE RIGHT!
CRIPES.
Peirce

IS THE PRINCIPAL HERE, MRS. SHIPULSKI? I NEED TO REPORT A DISTURBING INCIDENT.
OH, DEAR.
I'M NOT AT LIBERTY TO DISCUSS IT, BUT SUFFICE IT TO SAY MY **WARDROBE** WILL PROVIDE YOU WITH SOME CLUES ABOUT THE MATTER!
I UNDERSTAND, NATE. SAY NO MORE. I'LL GET PRINCIPAL NICHOLS.
THANK YOU, MY DEAR.
SIR, NATE WRIGHT IS BEING TEASED FOR WEARING A CAPE AND A STRANGE HAT.
WHAT? NO!
1/15
© 2007 by NEA, Inc.
Peirce

WHAT KIND OF A PERSON STEALS MONEY?
MOREOVER, WHAT KIND OF A PERSON STEALS MONEY FROM A KID? RIGHT OUT OF HIS LOCKER?
CLEARLY, I'M DEALING WITH A DERANGED INDIVIDUAL... A SICK MIND... A BORDERLINE PSYCHOPATH.
1/16
© 2007 by NEA, Inc.
WELCOME TO MY WORLD.
THE PRIME SUSPECT, OBVIOUSLY, IS MRS. GODFREY.
Peirce

WHAT'S UP, INSPECTOR GADGET?
MOCK ME IF YOU WANT, FRANCIS, BUT I'M ABOUT TO CATCH YOUR **THIEF**!

HA! RACHEL! I'VE CAUGHT YOU RED-HANDED!
RED-HAND..? **WHAT**?

I'VE BEEN STAKING OUT FRANCIS' LOCKER, KNOWING FULL WELL THAT WHOEVER **BURGLARIZED** IT THIS MORNING WOULD RETURN TO THE SCENE OF THE CRIME!
1/17

SPEAKING OF CRIMES, WHO DRESSED YOU?
I'M AFRAID, MY DEAR, THAT A FRISKING IS IN ORDER.
ROWR!
Peirce

TEDDY! WHERE WERE YOU THIS MORNING DURING HOMEROOM?
WHAT? WAIT A MINUTE!
YOU CAN'T THINK I STOLE FRANCIS' MONEY!
I'M JUST DOING MY JOB, DEAR CHAP.
EVERYONE'S A SUSPECT! WHY, THE VERY FIRST PERSON I INTER-VIEWED WAS MYSELF!
...AND I MUST SAY, I FOUND ME FAS-CINATING.
I THINK WE KNEW THAT ALREADY.
© 2007 by NEA, Inc.
1/18
Peirce

HEY!... HEY!
WHAT?
MY MONEY! IT WAS RIGHT HERE ALL ALONG! IT SLIPPED DOWN BEHIND THE SHELF WHERE I COULDN'T SEE IT!
HOLD IT, HOLD IT.
NAB!
HOW DO WE KNOW THIS IS REALLY YOUR TWENTY DOLLAR BILL? GIVE ME SOME PROOF THAT THIS IS ACTUALLY YOUR MONEY!
1/19
© 2007 by NEA, Inc.
IT'S IN A SANDWICH BAG WITH "FRANCIS BOOK FAIR MONEY" WRITTEN ON IT WITH A SHARPIE!
NOT GOOD ENOUGH. GIVE ME A SERIAL NUMBER
Peirce

ALL'S WELL THAT ENDS WELL, EH WHAT? ANOTHER CASE SOLVED!
CASE? THERE WAS NO CASE!
THE MONEY WAS RIGHT HERE IN MY LOCKER THE WHOLE TIME!
...WHICH YOU WOULDN'T HAVE REALIZED WITHOUT MY STELLAR DETECTIVE WORK!
BUT YOU DIDN'T DO ANYTHING! ALL YOU DID WAS WALK AROUND WITH THAT STUPID PIPE!
NO NEED TO THANK ME.
THANK YOU??
YOU'RE QUITE WELCOME, OLD BEAN.
1/20
Peirce

I'M HANDING BACK YOUR TESTS, PEOPLE!
I THINK IT'S SAFE TO SAY THEY ARE AN ACCURATE REFLECTION OF YOUR EFFORTS...
... OR **LACK** THEREOF!
SOME OF YOU CLEARLY STUDIED HARD AND WERE VERY WELL-PREPARED...
OTHERS RECEIVED PASSING GRADES, BUT ARE CAPABLE OF DOING MUCH BETTER...
...AND THE REST OF YOU? WELL, ALL I CAN SAY IS...
...PERHAPS YOUR GRADE WILL SERVE AS A **WAKE-UP CALL!**
A WAKE-UP CALL!
Z
FIRE

TEDDY! YO MAMA SMACK-DOWN!
YO MAMA SMACKDOWN? OKAY, LET'S SEE HERE...
1/22
YO MAMA IS SO UGLY, HER FACE IS CLOSED ON WEEKENDS.
YO MAMA IS SO FAT, WHEN SHE GOES TO THE MOVIES SHE SITS NEXT TO EVERYBODY!
© 2007 by NEA, Inc.
YO MAMA IS SO HAIRY, JANE GOODALL HAS SET UP BASE CAMP IN HER BATHROOM.
OKAY, YOU WIN.
Peirce

FRANCIS! YO MAMA SMACK-DOWN!
HUH? WHAT ARE YOU TALKING ABOUT?
I DROP A "YO MAMA" ON YOU...
YO MAMA'S SO FAT, WHEN SHE GETS ON AN ELEVATOR, SHE **HAS** TO GO DOWN!
1 23
...AND NOW YOU COME BACK AT ME!
WAIT, WAIT... MY MOTHER IS ACTUALLY QUITE SLENDER.
© 2007 by NEA, Inc.
NO, NO, NO.
MAYBE YOU'RE THINKING OF **TEDDY'S** MOM!
WHAT? HEY!

ARTUR! YO MAMA SMACK-DOWN!
GOOD! YES! WHAT IS?
JUST LISTEN: YO MAMA'S SO UGLY...
EXCUSE PLEASE, NATE. SHOULD NOT IT BE "YOUR MAMA"?
WELL... YEAH, BUT THIS IS, LIKE, SLANG.
AH! "SLANG" IS LIKE NICK-NAME, YES? WE FIND NICKNAME FOR TO MY MOTHER!
1/24
© 2007 by NEA, Inc.
ARTUR, TRY TO STAY ON TASK.
HOW ABOUT "CUBBY"?
Peirce

ARTUR, YOU REALLY AREN'T UNDERSTANDING THE CONCEPT OF THE YO MAMA SMACKDOWN.
YES. WHAT ARE YOU SAYING?
I'M SAYING IF YOU WANT TO GET ALONG IN LIFE, YOU'VE GOT TO LEARN HOW TO TALK A LITTLE SMACK!
SMACK. AH.
NOW PICK SOMEBODY AND SAY SOME-THING ABOUT THEIR MAMA!
HOKAY. PETER! YOUR MOTHER MAKES VERY DELICIOUS OATMEAL COOKIES!
1 25
© 2007 by NEA, Inc.
THANKS, DUDE.
ARTUR, ARTUR, ARTUR.
IS TRUE! THEY ARE LIP-SMACKIN' GOOD!
Peirce

WHAT'S UP, GENTS?
I'M TRYING TO TEACH ARTUR THE FINER POINTS OF THE YO MAMA SMACKDOWN.
AM NOT DOING GOOD SO FAR.
JUST WATCH ME, ARTUR! JUST DO WHAT I DO!
1/26
I'LL THROW DOWN SOME KILLER YO MAMAS AT THE NEXT PERSON TO COME AROUND THE CORNER!
Peirce
© 2007 by NEA, Inc.
THIS OUGHTA BE GOOD!
CH-CHESTER!
WHUT?

GO ON, NATE! YOU SAID YOU WERE GONNA DROP A "YO MAMA" ON CHESTER!
WHAT? NO! NO, I DIDN'T!
I DIDN'T SAY "YO MAMA"! I SAID... KOFF! ... I SAID "YO YO MA"!
YO YO MA IS A GREAT CELLO PLAYER! RIGHT, CHESTER OL' PAL?
YOU'RE WEIRD.
1/27
© 2007 by NEA, Inc.
YOU'RE GUT-LESS.
I'M ALIVE.
WHEN YOU'RE WEIRD, YOU MAKE ME WANT TO HIT YOU.
Peirce

HELLO?
NATE? THIS IS MRS. GODFREY.
UH... HI.
MAY I SPEAK TO YOUR FATHER, PLEASE?
DAD?... KOFF! IT'S MRS. GODFREY.
YOUR TEACHER?
BELLINGER AUTO MALL
HELLO?
YES! HELLO, MRS. GODFREY!
SPORTS
OH, REALLY? NO, I HADN'T HEARD ABOUT THAT! HOW INTERESTING!
1 28
MM HMM... YES, THAT DOES SOUND LIKE SOMETHING HE SHOULD HAVE MENTIONED!
I WILL!... I CERTAINLY WILL!... YES, YOU CAN BE SURE OF THAT!... THANK YOU FOR CALLING.
BOOP!
SHE WAS JUST ASKING ME TO HELP CHAPERONE A FIELD TRIP, BUT HE DOESN'T HAVE TO KNOW THAT.
CAN I GET YOU ANYTHING?
Peirce

FINALLY! GORDIE, WHERE HAVE YOU BEEN?
SORRY, ELLEN, I LOST TRACK OF TIME.
LOST TRACK OF TIME DOING WHAT?
ER... READING THE NEW ISSUE OF "FEMME FATALITY."
1/29
"FEMME FATALITY," DID YOU SAY?
YUP! HOT OFF THE PRESSES!
...THE OPERATIVE WORD BEING "HOT."
DID SOME-ONE MENTION "FEMME FATALITY"?
ROWR!
© 2007 by NEA, Inc.
Peirce

I JUST FINISHED THAT "FEMME FATALITY," NATE. BEST ISSUE **EVER**!
REALLY?

AFTER THE WOLF WARS IN THE KIEL GALAXY, FEMME RETURNS TO EARTH IN THE YEAR 2140!
1/30

...AND BECAUSE THE AVERAGE TEMPERATURE IS OVER ONE HUNDRED DEGREES, SHE SPENDS THE ENTIRE STORY... AHEM! ...DRESSED ACCORDINGLY!

I NEVER THOUGHT I'D SAY THIS, BUT... GOD BLESS GLOBAL WARMING!
AMEN, BROTHER!
HOO BOY.
Peirce

COME ON, GORDIE! WE'LL BE LATE FOR THE MOVIE!
HERE, GORDIE, YOU CAN LEAVE YOUR "FEMME FATALITY" WITH ME!
BE CAREFUL WITH IT, NATE!
DON'T WORRY! SHE'LL BE IN GOOD HANDS!
1/31
MY HANDS!
CAN I JUST PEEK AT THE COVER?
© 2007 by NEA, Inc.
PEIRCE

GORDIE WAS RIGHT! THAT WAS THE BEST ISSUE OF "FEMME FATALITY" EVER!
YOU'RE DONE WITH IT? YES!
MY TURN! LEMME SEE, LEMME SEE!
WHOA, WHOA! I'M ONLY DONE READING IT!
2/1
GAZING LONGINGLY AT THE MAGNIFICENT ART-WORK UNTIL EVERY IMAGE IS SEARED INTO MY BRAIN WILL TAKE MORE TIME!
© 2007 by NEA, Inc.
HOW MUCH MORE TIME?
DAYS. PERHAPS WEEKS.
ROWR!
Peirce

PLEASE CAN I LOOK AT "FEMME FATALITY"? PLEEEZ?
I'M NOT DONE YET.
JUST FOR TEN MINUTES? FIVE MINUTES?
DAD, LOOK AT YOURSELF! YOU'RE BEGGING!
2/2
YES, I'M BEGGING! WHEN IT COMES TO "FEMME FATALITY," I'LL BEG!
BUT FEMME WOULDN'T LIKE THAT, DAD. SHE'D THINK YOU WERE A WUSSY.
© 2007 by NEA, Inc.
SHE WOULD?
SHE TENDS TO DECAPITATE GUYS LIKE THAT.
Peirce

LOOK, DAD, "FEMME FATALITY" IS **MY** CRUSH! CAN'T YOU GET A CRUSH OF YOUR **OWN**!?
DON'T YOU LIKE KATIE COURIC? GO DROOL OVER KATIE COURIC!
KATIE COURIC?
BUT... SINCE SHE LEFT "TODAY," THE SPARK IS GONE.
MOVE ALONG, DAD.
2/3
© 2007 by NEA, Inc.
Peirce

207
MR. GALVIN?
NOK NOK
YES! HELLO THERE, NATE!
HI.
WHAT CAN I DO FOR YOU?
UM... I HAVE A QUESTION.
ABOUT THE HOME-WORK?
NO, IT... IT'S SORT OF HARD TO ASK.
NOW DON'T BE SHY, MY BOY! WHATEVER YOUR QUESTION, I'M SURE I CAN ANSWER IT!
AFTER ALL, I'M HERE TO HELP!
WELL... OKAY...
ARE THOSE YOUR REAL TEETH, OR DO YOU WEAR DENTURES?
2/4
CRIPES.
SAY DENTURES. I'VE GOT A DOLLAR RIDING ON THIS.
Peirce

CANDY CORN? WHERE'D YOU GET CANDY CORN?
IT'S MINE. I'VE BEEN SAVING IT SINCE HALLOWEEN.
HALLO-WEEN?
I MAKE MY HALLOWEEN CANDY LAST UNTIL VALENTINE'S DAY, MY VALENTINE'S CANDY LAST UNTIL EASTER...
...AND THEN I MAKE MY EASTER CANDY LAST UNTIL HALLOWEEN! I'VE GOT THE WHOLE YEAR COVERED!
IMPRESSIVE, YET FREAKISH.
YUMMY, YET STALE.
CRUNCH!
2/5
Peirce

I CAN'T BELIEVE YOU'RE STILL EATING YOUR WAY THROUGH YOUR HALLOWEEN CANDY!
WHAT'S THE BIG DEAL? I WANTED TO RATION IT OUT, THAT'S ALL!
BUT FRANCIS! FOR **THREE MONTHS**?
WELL, HOW LONG DID **YOUR** HALLOWEEN CANDY LAST?
MINE? UNTIL WEDNESDAY.
WEDNESDAY? LAST WEDNESDAY?
2/6
© 2007 by NEA, Inc.
WEDNESDAY, NOVEMBER 1ST.
IT WAS THE **SUGAR BUZZ** THAT LASTED 'TIL CHRISTMAS!
Peirce

SO FOR THE PAST THREE MONTHS YOU'VE BEEN HOARDING HALLOWEEN CANDY!
NOT HOARDING. MAKING IT LAST!
YOU NEVER SHARED ANY OF IT, RIGHT? YOU NEVER OFFERED ME ANY! THAT MEANS IT IS HOARDING!
OKAY, OKAY! I'LL GIVE YOU SOME-THING!
WHAT'S THIS?
MY NEIGHBOR IS AN ORTHO-DONTIST.
DENTAL FLOSS ISN'T CANDY!
IT'S MINT-FLAVORED. ENJOY.
© 2007 by NEA, Inc.
2/7
Peirce

I KNOW WHAT YOU'RE UP TO, NATE!
ME? WHAT?
YOU WERE OBVIOUSLY THINKING OF THROWING THAT SNOW-BALL AT ME!
WHAT? **NO**, I WASN'T! I WASN'T THINKING OF THAT AT **ALL**!
2/8
POW!
I WAS ACTUALLY PLANNING MY ESCAPE ROUTE!
peirce

LA TA DEE DUM DAH...
YOU HAVEN'T THROWN OUT A RUNNER AT SECOND IN ALL OUR YEARS IN LITTLE LEAGUE.
© 2007 by NEA, Inc.
2/9
Peirce

A TROMBONE, WRIGHT? A TROMBONE? WHAT'S THAT ALL ABOUT?
ARE THEY HAVING ORCHESTRA PRACTICE OUTDOORS NOW? HEY, WHERE'S THE TUBA SECTION?
SCOOP!
...OR ARE YOU JUST PLANNING TO PLAY A CONCERT FOR... UH... HEY, WHAT ARE YOU...?
PACK
PACK
PACK
2/10
© 2007 by NEA, Inc.
BLAAAT!!
Peirce

HALLO, GUYS! I JOIN YOU, HOKAY?
ARTUR! I DIDN'T KNOW YOU COULD SKATE!
OH, MOST DEFINITE! I LIKE TO SKATE!
BUT WHERE'S YOUR STICK?
I HAVE NO STICK! AM NOT PLAY ICE HOCKEY.
ARE THOSE... FIGURE SKATES?
OF COURSE, YES!
DUDE, YOU CAN'T WEAR THOSE!
SNICKER!
BUT WHY NOT?
BECAUSE THEY... WELL, IT'S... YOU JUST...
ARTURRR!...
ARTUR, MY COACH SAYS MY FOOTWORK WILL IMPROVE IF I PRACTICE WITH A PARTNER!
WILL YOU SKATE WITH ME?
2/11
WELL, THAT'S A PUCK IN THE TEETH.
EXCEPT WE LOST OUR PUCK A HALF HOUR AGO.
peirce

WHAT'S UP, AMIGO?
I'M MAKING A VALENTINE FOR SHEILA.
OOH! LET ME TAKE A LOOK! I'LL GIVE YOU MY PROFESSIONAL OPINION!
PROFESSIONAL OPINION?
FRANCIS, I'M THE **KING** OF HOMEMADE VALENTINES! REMEMBER THE CARD I MADE FOR JENNY LAST YEAR? THE ONE WITH THE POEM?
2/12
"JENNY, JENNY, JENNY, JENNY. YOU SLAY ME LIKE SOUTH PARK'S KENNY."
AN INSTANT CLASSIC!
PEIRCE

I'M WRITING A VALENTINE POEM FOR JENNY, AND I WANT TO TOP THE ONE I WROTE LAST YEAR.
THAT SHOULDN'T BE DIFFICULT.
"YOU'RE SO FOXALICIOUS, AND I'M SO... HMMM...
WHAT RHYMES WITH "FOXA-LICIOUS"?
"STUPID."
2/13
© 2007 by NEA, Inc.
THAT DOESN'T RHYME!
IT'S THE RIGHT WORD.
peirce

You've known me now
For many years,
But never have we dated.
For reasons
I don't understand,
You think our love ill-fated.
But Jenny,
I'm your destiny.
One day we will be mated.
And then you'll know
Just what it's like
To say that you've been "Nated."
2/14
Peirce

HI, MRS. CZERWICKI!
HELLO, NATE.
HOW WAS YOUR VALENTINE'S DAY?
OH, WAS YESTERDAY VALENTINE'S DAY?
WHY, I HAD NO IDEA!! THERE WEREN'T ANY CARDS OR FLOWERS FOR ME AT MY HOUSE!
2/15
© 2007 by NEA, Inc.
SOMEONE MUST HAVE BEEN BUSY WATCHING THE HISTORY CHANNEL!
YOU KNOW WHAT, I THINK I'LL GO SIT DOWN.
Peirce

HM? WHAT'S THIS?
THERE'S SOME SORT OF **NOTE** IN MY POCKET!
?
?
COULD SOME LOVELY LASS HAVE SLIPPED ME A **VALENTINE** THE OTHER DAY WITHOUT ME **REALIZING** IT?
2/16
© 2007 by NEA, Inc.
"THIS GARMENT INSPECTED BY NUMBER 62."
OOH! I HEAR SHE'S **HOT**!
Peirce

JENNY, I WANT YOU TO KNOW THAT I UNDERSTAND WHY YOU DIDN'T GIVE ME A VALENTINE THIS YEAR!
OH?
IT'S BECAUSE YOU'RE **SCARED** OF **LIKING** ME TOO MUCH! IT'S EASIER TO **DENY** YOUR FEELINGS THAN TO **ADMIT** THEM!
THOSE SORTS OF POWERFUL EMOTIONS CAN BE OVER-WHELMING!
2/17
SO CAN NAUSEA.
NOW, NOW, MY SWEET! WE CALL THAT "**LOVE-SICKNESS**"!
PEIRCE

WHAT'D YOU GET?
A 98.
YOU DID? THAT'S GREAT!
NO, IT ISN'T. IT'S AWFUL.
AWFUL? WHAT ARE YOU TALKING ABOUT?
THE OTHER SHOE IS ABOUT TO DROP.
WHAT OTHER SHOE?
NATE...
I WAS DELIGHTED, ABSOLUTELY DELIGHTED, WITH YOUR PERFORMANCE ON THIS LAST TEST.
THIS PROVES THAT, WITH HARD WORK, YOU'RE CAPABLE OF THIS CALIBER OF WORK ON EVERY TEST. I HOPE YOU REMEMBER THAT.
I CERTAINLY WILL.
AH.
OH, HOW I HATE HER.

WHAT ARE WE DOING IN ART TODAY, MR. ROSA?
MAKING A MESS.
TURNING MY CLASSROOM INTO AN ABSOLUTE PIGSTY THAT'LL TAKE THREE HOURS TO CLEAN UP AFTER SCHOOL, MAKING MY BACK EVEN MORE SORE THAN IT ALREADY IS!
MR. ROSA?
CLAY SCULPTURE.
YES!
I NEED AN ASPIRIN.
2/19
© 2007 by NEA, Inc.
Peirce

YESSS! CLAY! CLAY IS MY FAVORITE ART PROJECT OF THE YEAR!
REMEMBER THAT DRAGON I MADE LAST YEAR? THAT, IF I DO SAY SO MYSELF, BELONGED IN A MUSEUM!
I'M A MASTER OF SCULPTURE! I'M THE MICHELANGELO OF SCULPTURE!
2/20
© 2007 by NEA, Inc.
DUDE. MICHEL-ANGELO WAS THE MICHEL-ANGELO OF SCULPTURE.
WAS. PAST TENSE.
BAM BAM BAM BAM BAM
Peirce

MICHELANGELO SAID THAT IN EVERY BLOCK OF MARBLE, THERE'S A HUMAN FORM STRUG-GLING TO GET OUT!
WELL, SAME THING WITH THIS HUNK OF CLAY! INSIDE IT IS A HUMAN FORM STRUGGLING TO GET OUT!
2/21
THAT'S QUITE A STRUGGLE.
NICE MANATEE!
Peirce

I'M SCULPTING A GRIFFIN!
A GRIFFIN?
YOU KNOW, FROM GREEK MYTHOLOGY! HALF LION, HALF EAGLE!
2/22
THAT'S SUPPOSED TO BE A GRIFFIN?
IT LOOKS MORE LIKE A MUFFIN!
© 2007 by NEA, Inc.
IT'S A GRUFFIN!
HALF ANIMAL, HALF BREAD PRODUCT!
I CAN'T CREATE UNDER THESE CON-DITIONS.
Peirce

MR. ROSA, MY CLAY'S GETTING ALL CRUMBLY!
IT'S DRYING OUT. YOU NEED TO KEEP IT MOIST.
HOCCH...
PTOO!
2/23
© 2007 by NEA, Inc.
NATE, THERE'S A MARVELOUS INVENTION OVER THERE CALLED A "FAUCET."
I'M NOT THIRSTY.
SMOOSH
SMASH
MASH
Peirce

JENNY, M'LADY! WOULD YOU CARE TO BE THE SUB-JECT OF A SCULPTURAL PORTRAIT?
ME?
YEAH! I WANT TO SCULPT YOUR FACE!... IF THAT'S OKAY WITH YOU, I MEAN!
WELL... SURE! THAT WOULD BE FINE!
2/24
SMAK!
© 2007 by NEA, Inc.
MMPH!
NOW HOLD STILL WHILE I PEEL IT OFF!
Peirce

ONE DOLLAR? THAT'S NOT BAD!
A BARGAIN, MY DEAR! A STONE-COLD STEAL!
CARICATURES by NATE $1.00
WHAT THE HECK? I'LL TAKE ONE!
EXCELLENT!
DO YOU WANT ME TO POSE, OR...?
HANG ON, HANG ON...
DONE!
WHAT THE...? THAT DOESN'T LOOK ANYTHING LIKE ME!
IT'S NOT YOU! IT'S GEORGE W. BUSH!
IT'S THE ONLY CARICATURE I KNOW HOW TO DRAW!
IDIOT!
NOT ONLY DIDN'T I GET PAID, I DON'T THINK I MADE HIS EARS BIG ENOUGH.
2
25
peirce

MRS. GODFREY, I CAN'T CONCENTRATE ON THE TEST BECAUSE NATE KEEPS GRINDING HIS TEETH!
KRONNK KRONNK KRONNK
I CAN'T HELP IT! I GRIND MY TEETH WHEN I'M STRESSED OUT!
THEN DO SOMETHING TO DEAL WITH THE STRESS!
THUNK THUNK THUNK THUNK THUNK THUNK THUNK
2/26
© 2007 by NEA, Inc.
MRS. GODFREY, I CAN'T CONCENTRATE ON THE TEST BECAUSE NATE IS BONKING HIMSELF IN THE HEAD WITH AN EMPTY SODA BOTTLE.
UNK THUNK THUNK THUN UNK
AAHHHH...
Peirce

WILL YOU **PLEASE** STOP BONKING YOURSELF WITH THAT STUPID BOTTLE!?
CHILL OUT, GINA. IT'S RELAXING.
THUNK THUNK THUNK THUNK
WELL, **I** DON'T THINK...
THUNK
2/27
...IT...
THUNK THUNK THUNK THUNK THUNK THUNK
THUNK
THUNK
AAHHHHH...
THUNK
THUNK
IT'S LIKE HAVING A DART GUN.
Peirce

WHAT A LOUSY DAY! FIRST I FAILED THE MATH TEST, THEN I TWISTED MY ANKLE IN GYM...
...AND THEN...
THUNK!
THUNK THUNK THUNK THUNK THUNK THUNK THUNK
WHAT WAS I SAYING?
I'M A HEALER!
2/28
© 2007 by NEA, Inc.

WHY ARE YOU GOING AROUND HITTING EVERYONE WITH THAT PLASTIC BOTTLE?
JUST SPREADING THE JOY, FRANCIS!
THUNK THUNK THUNK THUNK
I'M USING MY BOTTLE TO **HELP** PEOPLE! I'M EASING THEIR PSYCHIC PAIN! I, MY FRIEND, AM A **HEALER**!
A HEALER? SNORT! NOW I'VE SEEN EVERYTHING!
BONK BONK BONK BONK BON
HOW MUCH DO I OWE YOU?
ONE BUCK!
$ $
CORRECTION: **NOW** I'VE SEEN EVERY-THING.
MAKE IT TWO!
'KAY.
$

WHAT?
YOU HEARD ME!
CAN'T BELIEVE
U DID THAT!
BUT I DIDN'T!
YOU JUST SAID SO!
YOU ARE BEING SUC
THUNK THUNK THUNK THUNK THUNK THUNK THUNK
THUNK THUNK THUNK THUNK THUNK THUNK THUNK THUNK
3/2
© 2007 by NEA, Inc.
WHAT WERE WE ARGUING ABOUT?
SIGH... I HAVE NO IDEA.
I HAVE A GIFT!
Peirce

IF THAT BOTTLE IS AS SOOTHING AS YOU SAY, IT'LL WORK ON ANYONE!... EVEN CHESTER!
CH... CHESTER?
THUNK
THUNK
THUNK
THUNK
THUNK
THUNK
HE'S RIGHT OVER THERE! GO GIVE HIM A BONK ON THE FOREHEAD AND PROVE IT!
WELL... OKAY.
SHOVE!
BONK!
SQUONK!
3/3
© 2007 by NEA, Inc.
SHOULD I TAKE YOU TO THE NURSE OR THE "INDUSTRIAL ARTS" TEACHER?
Peirce

HI, MAY I SPEAK TO CHIEF METEOROLOGIST WINK SUMMERS, PLEASE?
WINK! NATE WRIGHT HERE!
GOOD FORECAST LAST NIGHT, WINK! YOU ACTUALLY GOT IT **RIGHT** FOR A CHANGE!
LISTEN, THOUGH, I DON'T THINK YOU SHOULD WEAR THAT TWEED BLAZER ANYMORE. IT JUST CALLS ATTENTION TO HOW FAT YOU ARE.
PLUS, YOU GOT A LITTLE TONGUE-TIED DURING THE RADAR SEGMENT. I WAS LIKE: WHAT'S UP WITH WINK TONIGHT? IS HE **DRUNK?**
BUT THAT'S NOT WHY I'M CALLING, WINK. I'M CALLING TO LET YOU KNOW THAT SOMETHING MIGHTY FUNKY IS GOING ON WITH YOUR "HAIR REPLACEMENT SYSTEM."
IT LOOKS BAD. FRANKLY, IT LOOKS LIKE THERE'S A...
BEEP!
HE PUT A TIME LIMIT ON HIS ANSWERING MACHINE, SO NOW I HAVE TO LEAVE MY MESSAGES IN ONE-MINUTE CHUNKS.
boop
boop
boop
boop
boop
I'M GUESSING HE ALSO HAS "CALLER I D"
...LIKE THERE'S A DEAD CAT LYING ON YOUR HEAD.
3/4
peirce

CHECKMATE!
ARRRGH! I CAN NEVER BEAT YOU!
I JUST DON'T GET IT! WHY ARE YOU, OF ALL PEOPLE, SO GOOD AT CHESS?
WHAT DO YOU MEAN, "OF ALL PEOPLE"?
3/5
IT'S JUST THAT... MOST PEOPLE WHO ARE GOOD AT CHESS ARE USUALLY... THEY'RE USUALLY...
...GOOD AT SOME-THING ELSE?
YES! EXACTLY!
HEY! WHO ASKED YOU?
© 2007 by NEA, Inc.
Peirce

DON'T YOU THINK IT'S KIND OF WEIRD THAT NATE IS SUCH A CHESS PHENOM?
3/6
I MEAN, YOU'D EXPECT SOMEONE WHO'S SO GOOD AT CHESS TO BE, LIKE, REALLY SMART, RIGHT?
BUT HE'S JUST THE OPPOSITE! HE'S CLUELESS! MOST OF THE TIME HE HAS NO IDEA WHAT'S GOING ON!
NO OFFENSE.
HUH?
Peirce

AH-HA! IT SAYS IT RIGHT HERE: PEOPLE WHO ARE GIFTED AT CHESS ARE USUALLY GIFTED IN OTHER AREAS!
...LIKE MATH, FOR EXAMPLE! OR MUSIC!
WELL, THERE YOU GO! THAT'S ME! I'M VERY MUSICAL!
YOU?
HAVE YOU FORGOTTEN I PLAY THE TROMBONE?
HAVE YOU FORGOTTEN THAT THE BAND DIRECTOR SWITCHED YOU TO CYMBALS?
BECAUSE HE COULD TELL I'M A PER-CUSSION PRODIGY!
3/7
© 2007 by NEA, Inc.
Peirce

MR. ROSA, WHY DO YOU THINK NATE'S SO GOOD AT CHESS?
HE HAS A GIFT, THAT'S ALL!
EVERYONE'S GIFTED AT SOMETHING, FRANCIS!
REALLY?
WHAT ARE YOU GIFTED AT?
I JUST MADE A TEACHER CRY.
3/8
© 2007 by NEA, Inc.
Peirce

MR. ROSA SAYS EVERY-ONE'S GIFTED AT SOMETHING. I'M GIFTED WITH A PHOTOGRAPHIC MEMORY... NATE'S GIFTED AT CHESS...
...AMONG OTHER THINGS!
WHAT ABOUT YOU, TEDDY? WHAT'S YOUR GIFT?
I CAN DRINK A CARTON OF CHOCOLATE MILK, THEN BLOW IT OUT MY NOSE!
DUDE, WASN'T THAT AN ACCIDENT?
NO, THE "MOUNTAIN DEW CODE RED" WAS AN ACCIDENT. THE CHOCO-LATE MILK WAS ON PURPOSE.
GROSS.
© 2007 by NEA, Inc.
PEIRCE

I'M STILL INTRIGUED BY THE QUESTION OF WHY YOU'RE SO GOOD AT CHESS.
MAYBE YOU INHERITED IT! IS YOUR DAD GOOD AT CHESS?
MY DAD? HEH HEH HA HA
HA HA HA HA HA HA HA HA HO HO HA HO
A SIMPLE "NO" WOULD HAVE BEEN SUFFICIENT.
HA HA HO HA HA HA
"YAHTZEE," MAYBE!
HA HO HA H
3/10
© 2007 by NEA, Inc.
Peirce

BRRRRRR..
COACH! IT'S FREEZING OUT HERE!
COLD?
I'LL WARM YOU UP!
KRAK!
RUN THAT ONE DOWN!
UH OH...
LOOK OUT!
WHAM!
WANT ME TO... *CHUCKLE*... GET YOU SOME ICE?
I HATE SPRING TRAINING...
PEIRCE

WHAT'S WITH THE CAMERA?
I'VE JOINED THE YEAR-BOOK STAFF! I'M IN CHARGE OF CANDIDS!
BUT YOU DON'T KNOW ANYTHING ABOUT PHOTOGRAPHY!
WELL... I'LL JUST HAVE TO LEARN ON THE JOB.
YOU NEED A MENTOR.
YES!... A MENTOR! AND I KNOW JUST THE PERSON!
3/12
© 2007 by NEA, Inc.
RRINNG!
MOTHER! PHONE!
FIRE TORPEDOES, MISTER SULU.
AYE, CAPTAIN.
Peirce

SCHOOL PICTURE GUY!
IN THE FLESH, KID! THE MASTER HAS ARRIVED TO TUTOR THE APPRENTICE!
SO YOU'VE DECIDED TO BE A PHOTOGRAPHER, MY LAD! AN ADMIRABLE PROFESSION! A NOBLE CALLING!
HOW WELL I REMEMBER WHEN I WAS FIRST BITTEN BY THE SHUTTER BUG! YES, AMIGO, I RECALL IT VIVIDLY!
3/13
© 2007 by NEA, Inc.
STORY TIME.
HEADS TURNED THE DAY I VENTURED UNCERTAINLY INTO THE YEARBOOK MEETING...
PEIRCE

TAKE A LOOK, KID! EVERYWHERE AROUND YOU, THERE ARE MOMENTS HAPPENING! THEY HAPPEN, AND THEN THEY'RE GONE!
AS A PHOTOGRAPHER, THOUGH, YOU HAVE THE POWER TO MAKE THOSE MOMENTS LIVE FOREVER!!
THAT'S THE NUMBER ONE GOAL OF TAKING GOOD CANDIDS, KID: CAPTURING A MOMENT IN TIME!
I THOUGHT THE NUMBER ONE GOAL WAS CATCHING PEOPLE WITH STUPID LOOKS ON THEIR FACES.
TRUE. BUT WE DON'T SPEAK OF THAT.
3/14
© 2007 by NEA, Inc.
Peirce

OKAY, KID, FIRST ASSIGNMENT: LET'S GET A FEW CANDIDS OF SOME TEACHERS!
OOH! HOW ABOUT MR. GALVIN?
HIM? I'VE SEEN CADAVERS WITH MORE LIFE!
HE'S PLENTY LIVELY! YOU JUST HAVE TO GIVE HIM A JUMP START!
3/15
SAY, ISN'T THAT GRETA VAN SUSTEREN?
WHERE?
KID, YOU'RE A NATURAL.
KLIK!
KLIK!
peirce

I WANT TO GET A CANDID OF THAT JERK TYLER HINCKLEY LOOKING STUPID, BUT HE'S JUST SITTING THERE!
PATIENCE, GRASSHOPPER! PATIENCE!
REMEMBER RULE #17 OF CANDID PHOTOGRAPHY!
WHAT'S RULE #17?
GIVE A BOY - ANY BOY - ENOUGH TIME, AND HE WILL EVENTUALLY PICK HIS NOSE!
3/16
© 2007 by NEA, Inc.
SQUEE SQUEE
JACKPOT.
KLIK!
Peirce

I SHOT A WHOLE ROLL OF CANDIDS, AND ALL OF THEM ARE BOR-ING.
ARE YOU KIDDING? MY LAD, THIS IS A GOLD MINE!
YOU'RE FORGETTING THE SECRET OF YEARBOOK CANDIDS: IT'S ALL ABOUT THE CAPTION!
3/17
SLAP THE PROPER CAPTION UNDERNEATH THIS ORDINARY PHOTO OF MRS. GODFREY, AND WE'RE TALKIN' MAGIC!
Peirce
© 2007 by NEA, Inc.
HOW ABOUT "█████ █████ █████"?
GOOD! TOTALLY IN-APPROPRIATE, BUT GOOD!

FORTUNE COOKIE?
THAT REMAINS TO BE SEEN.
KRAK!
WHADDA YA MEAN?
ARRGH! THIS IS WHAT I MEAN!
3/18
THIS IS NOT A FORTUNE! IT'S JUST SOME LAME SAYING!
A FORTUNE IS SUPPOSED TO TELL YOU, "ONE DAY YOU'LL BE RICH" OR "TODAY WILL BE YOUR LUCKY DAY"! IT'S SUPPOSED TO PREDICT THE FUTURE!
DOES THIS PREDICT THE FUTURE? NO! SO IT'S NOT A FORTUNE! CALLING 'EM "FORTUNE COOKIES" IS WRONG!
HERE, YOU TAKE IT! I DON'T WANT IT!
!
TRIP!
"YOU ARE EASILY ANNOYED BY MATTERS OF LITTLE CONSEQUENCE."
WHO PUT THAT THERE?
Peirce

...SO THEN MRS. GODFREY GOES: "PEOPLE, I HAVE A VERY IMPORTANT DATE TO TELL YOU ABOUT."
...AND THEN NATE GOES: "REALLY? WHO'S THE LUCKY GUY?"
HEH HEH
HA HA HA
HA HA HA HA
HA HA HO HO
HEE HA HA HA
3/19
© 2007 by NEA, Inc.
TRUST ME, IT WAS FUNNY!
THE PRINCIPAL WILL SEE YOU NOW.
Peirce

NATE, I UNDERSTAND YOU WERE DISRUPTIVE IN MRS. GODFREY'S CLASS.
I JUST CRACKED A LITTLE JOKE IS ALL!
IT WAS INAPPROPRIATE.
I'M A **KIDDER**, THAT'S ALL! I LIKE TO JOKE AROUND! THAT'S NOT INAPPROPRIATE!
I MEAN, IS IT INAPPROPRIATE WHEN I KID WITH **YOU** ABOUT YOUR MORBID OBESITY?
3/20
© 2007 by NEA, Inc.
SIGH...
OF **COURSE** NOT! BECAUSE FAT PEOPLE ARE SO **JOLLY**!
PAT PAT
Peirce

THIS YOUNG MAN IS HERE FOR DETENTION.
OH, DEAR. WHAT IS IT THIS TIME, NATE?
HE MADE A JOKE AT MY EXPENSE.
WHAT? I DID MAKE A JOKE, BUT IT WASN'T AT YOUR EXPENSE!
I WASN'T LAUGHING AT YOU, I WAS LAUGHING WITH YOU!
3/21
© 2007 by NEA, Inc.
EXCEPT I WASN'T LAUGHING.
WELL, THAT'S YOUR PROBLEM! HOW IS THAT MY FAULT?
Peirce

"ONE, TWO, THREE, FOUR... I DECLARE A THUMB WAR."
HOLD IT, HOLD IT! THUMB WRESTLING?
LET'S HAVE A REAL TEST OF STRENGTH: ARM WRESTLING!
SLAM!
3/22
© 2007 by NEA, Inc.
"ONE, TWO, THREE, FOUR... I DECLARE A THUMB WAR."
YOU'RE HURTING ME.
Peirce

WHAT ARE YOU GUYS DOING?
THUMB WRESTLING!
WANNA GIVE IT A TRY, JENNY M'LADY?
HOW DO YOU DO IT?
WELL, FIRST WE JOIN HANDS...
UH HUH...
3/23
© 2007 by NEA, Inc.
THEN WE TAKE A MOMENT TO ACKNOWLEDGE THE OBVIOUS ROMANTIC ELECTRICITY...
ROWR!
OH BROTHER
Peirce

"ONE, TWO, THREE, FOUR... I DECLARE A THUMB WAR."
HA! OHH, THAT WAS TOO EASY!
GAAHHH! OW OW OW OW OW!!
NEVER THUMB WKESILE SOMEONE WITH SHARP FINGER-NAILS.
I WON.

WHOOO! WHAT A WORKOUT!
THAT WAS FUN!
WHAT WAS FUN?
REMEMBER THAT STORY YOU TOLD ME YES-TERDAY, DAD?
NO, WHAT STORY DID I TELL YOU YESTERDAY?
HOW WHEN YOU WERE A KID, YOU USED TO SPEND HOURS HITTING ROCKS WITH A BASEBALL BAT!
3/25
WELL, WE JUST DID KIND OF THE SAME THING!
RIGHT! KIND OF!
AH! LET ME GUESS!
INSTEAD OF A WOODEN BAT LIKE I USED TO HAVE, YOU USED A METAL BAT!
NO, WE DIDN'T USE A BAT AT ALL!
WE USED YOUR GOLF CLUBS!
! !
SPEAKING OF GOLF, I DON'T THINK I'LL EVER TAKE IT UP.
SAME HERE. TOO STRESS-FUL.
Peirce

MRS. GODFREY, CAN TEDDY AND I BE PARTNERS FOR THE CIVIL WAR REPORT?
I DON'T THINK SO, NATE.
BUT YOU **NEVER** LET US WORK TOGETHER!
THAT'S NOT TRUE.
I LET THE TWO OF YOU PAIR UP LAST YEAR FOR YOUR PAPER ON GIOVANNI DA VERRAZANO!
3/26
WHO?
SOUNDS FRENCH.
YOU'RE MAKING MY POINT, BOYS.
Peirce

ALL RIGHT, BOYS. I'LL PROBABLY REGRET THIS, BUT... YOU MAY WORK TOGETHER ON THE CIVIL WAR REPORT.
YESS!
GO TO THE LIBRARY AND BEGIN YOUR RESEARCH.
RIGHT!
...AND MAKE GOOD CHOICES!
"SPORTS ILLUSTRATED" OR "NATIONAL GEOGRAPHIC"?
"NATIONAL GEO-GRAPHIC." LET'S TROLL FOR NUDITY!
3/27
© 2007 by NEA, Inc.
Peirce

GINA? TEDDY AND I NEED YOUR HELP OVER IN THE REFERENCE SECTION.
REALLY? SURE, I'LL HELP YOU!
ARE YOU HAVING TROUBLE PICKING A TOPIC? THE CIVIL WAR PROVIDES SO MANY THINGS TO WRITE ABOUT!
WE JUST NEED YOUR OPINION.
3/28
I'M TRYING TO DECIDE BETWEEN WILLIAM TECUMSEH SHERMAN AND...
IS THAT FOOTBALL OVER THE EDGE?
© 2007 by NEA, Inc.
CRIPES.
IT'S A TOUCH-DOWN, RIGHT?
HEY! NO LOBBY-ING!
Peirce

WHAT ARE YOU FOOLS DOING PLAYING TABLE FOOTBALL? YOU'RE SUPPOSED TO BE RESEARCHING YOUR CIVIL WAR REPORT!
SHUT UP, GINA.
SHUT UP? SHUT UP? YOU CAN'T MAKE ME SHUT UP! YOU CAN'T MAKE ME SHUT UP!
FLIK!
POINK!
OW!
SHE'S RIGHT.
NICE TRY, THOUGH.

ALL RIGHT, BOYS, LET'S HEAR YOUR CIVIL WAR TOPIC.
HA! THEY DON'T EVEN **HAVE** ONE, MRS. GODFREY!
THEY DIDN'T DO A **BIT** OF RESEARCH IN THE LIBRARY! THEY SPENT THE ENTIRE PERIOD PLAYING **TABLE FOOTBALL!**
3/30
OUR REPORT IS ON THE BATTLE OF SHILOH: APRIL 6TH AND 7TH, 1862.
WONDERFUL!
WERE YOU SAYING SOMETHING, GINA?
YES, GINA, WERE YOU SAYING SOMETHING?
PEIRCE

HOW DID YOU DOLTS COME UP WITH SUCH A GOOD TOPIC? YOU DIDN'T EVEN CRACK A BOOK!
EASY! TEDDY'S DAD IS A CIVIL WAR BUFF!
HE'S BEEN TELLING ME ABOUT ALL THE DIFFERENT BATTLES SINCE I WAS A BABY! HE BUILDS MODELS OF CIVIL WAR BATTLEFIELDS IN OUR BASEMENT!
I COULD WRITE A REPORT ON THE BATTLE OF SHILOH IN MY SLEEP!
...WHICH IS WHY I CHOSE HIM AS MY PARTNER!
3/31
© 2007 by NEA, Inc.
RELAX, DUDE. WE'LL PUT YOUR NAME FIRST ON THE TITLE PAGE.
RIGHT, AND... WAIT. WHAT?

"IN LIKE A LION, OUT LIKE A LAMB"!
EH?
WHAT IS?
IT'S A SAYING, ARTUR! ABOUT THE WEATHER DURING MARCH!
AT THE BEGINNING OF MARCH, THE WEATHER IS STILL WINTRY AND FIERCE! SO: "IN LIKE A LION"!
BUT AT THE END OF MARCH, THE WEATHER IS ALL WARM AND CALM! SO: "OUT LIKE A LAMB"!
AND IT'S TRUE! MARCH IS OVER, AND THE WEATHER IS ALL MILD AND...
...AND...
4/1
IS ALSO ANOTHER SAYING: "APRIL FOOL'S!"
THIS IS AN OUTRAGE.
Peirce